My Friend,
Jane

By Megan Ravenhall

Contents

Preface	Preface	3
Chapter 1	My Friend Jane	7
Chapter 2	13 months, 24 pounds	9
Chapter 3	Postman Pat and his Black and White Cat	20
Chapter 4	Zak	31
Chapter 5	Smile	40
Chapter 6	Friday the 13th..	52
Chapter 7	Ward 13	61
Chapter 8	The choice	72
Chapter 9	The Little Red Balloon	81
Chapter 10	Relapse	96
Chapter 11	St Andrews	114
Chapter 12	Guilt	129
Chapter 13	Still Being Written	141
	Thirteen Thank Yous	157

Preface

There are many common fallacies surrounding eating disorders: assumptions of what causes them, stereotypes for who tends to struggle with them and what to say to those in the depths of one. Some argue that they are the result of trauma, the fruit of a childhood stained in abuse or the consequence of sexual assault or domestic violence. Some believe that they occur naturally when one has a genetic predisposition to mental illness or has experienced a lifetime of self-harm. Others argue that they are a troubled soul's way of coping with the world, a way for a person who struggles to exert control in many areas of their life to exercise complete agency over something, that something being food.

There is the over-achiever, the anxious teenager, the single Mum who just wants to feel sexy and "skinny" is the only way she knows how. There is the diet culture that pollutes every magazine and every social media platform with unrealistic body shapes and fitness goals. There are those who believe everything they see and put immense amounts of pressure on themselves to try and achieve this unrealistic, airbrushed version of celebrities and fitness fanatics who they follow on social media. These are all realities for eating disorder sufferers, but there isn't a "one size fits all" – every case is different and every individual is unique.

There are hundreds of thousands of ways a person can be made to feel less than adequate. In fact, every eating disorder sufferer has their very own story to tell. Each person has a family and they would not exist without them – whether actively involved in their recovery, or not. Each person has triggers or things which, when said, do more harm than good in aiding the progress of their recovery. For such a prevalent issue, especially in Western Culture, eating disorders are a delicate matter. Though the sufferer tends to be incredibly headstrong, their psyche is extremely fragile and susceptible to other peoples' observations or comments. There is a clear difference between a person saying 'I'm anorexic', because they lost a couple of pounds on a two- week diet, and a twelve-year-old saying 'no, there's nothing wrong with me' whilst sat in a wheelchair as their organs (not yet fully developed) start to fail because of an active decision - that blew out of their control - to restrict calorie intake.

Diet culture is prolific on every social media platform, in every magazine and even in casual conversation. Still, to this day, society tends to judge every book by its cover, though the values that are instilled from a young age encourage looking beneath the surface to make a true judgement of character. No-one knows what to say because we do not talk about it as a society. Still, in the twenty-first century, it is almost a taboo. It is joked about, but rarely examined in closer detail because, collectively, we lack a comprehensive education of it. It makes us feel uncomfortable and, instead of encouraging a discussion about it, we sweep it under the carpet. Everyone is guilty of jumping to conclusions; initial instincts based on the five senses are an inherent part of being human. We cannot taste a person or feel a person when we first meet them and so we are forced to use what senses we have left – smell, sound and sight. It is no surprise, therefore, that we tend to be an "aesthetically assumptive" race. Yet, judging any person on their weight and physical appearance without knowing them is inexcusably and fundamentally, wrong.

Amidst all this speculation of what to say and what not to say, what to believe and what not to believe, there is one undeniable misconception, a misconception which, in the case of this story's protagonist, Jane, took a long time for those who loved her to fully understand. It is simple, but it is quite possibly one of the most frequently misunderstood aspects of an eating disorder: the misconception that suffering from anorexia, bulimia, orthorexia or any EDNOS* is a choice.

Nobody chooses to have an eating disorder.
Let me say that again.
Nobody chooses to have an eating disorder.

A person may choose to go on a diet. They may choose to cut carbs or workout five times a week. There is choice every time they go to the supermarket and choice when they browse restaurant menus or decide which cocktail fits their fancy. A person chooses to smoke cigarettes and play guitar just as they choose to cut off all of their hair or choose to get a tattoo.

Any person may choose to alter their lifestyle in a way which is drastically different from their current situation. However, whether or not this manifests itself into patterns of disordered eating, depends wholly on the unique individual making that choice.

Nobody chooses to fall victim to their own thought processes, to wake up every morning and detest the person that looks back at them in the mirror. This is unexplained – a chemical imbalance that goes beyond choice – and sometimes seems completely absurd. There may be trigger factors that cause a person to seek to control their diet and exercise as a means of dealing with, for example, trauma, but nobody chooses to feel a paralysing sense of guilt every time they put something in their mouth.

This feeling, this parasite, has many names. Psychiatrists often try to get their patient to refer to their eating disorder as a separate entity in an attempt to dissociate the disease from the individual. They emphasise that "she" or "he", "they" or "it" is not a part of the individual. It is not them, therefore, they must stop referring to the illness as such. It is easy for the sufferer to believe that their actions, the choices they make whilst in the depths of their struggle, are their own, but one of the first things the psychiatrist tells their patient is:

this is not your fault.

This is not a choice.

Professionals often explain the illness to family and friends as being like a cancer. Would you tell a person with cancer to stop growing abnormal cells uncontrollably? No, of course not. So why is it, then, that we tell an eating disorder sufferer to 'just eat'?

This tale will not be prefaced with a trigger warning.

Eating disorders are not attractive, just as they are not a choice. They strip the soul bare of all personality, and take away the parts that make you, you. They don't stop when a person is weight-restored and the pathway to recovery is far from easy. Once a person's mind-set changes so drastically, it is almost impossible to teach them to un-think in a particular way. There will always be a residual echo; a reminder of the time when food wasn't a necessity, it was the enemy.

The cure is the thing most feared.

This is what makes it such a brutal and unforgiving battle. In order to survive, the sufferer must absorb their nemesis, both physically and mentally. They must find the strength to fight from a body which is often so severely malnourished it is going into shutdown.

The struggle is infinite, so I am told, but there are survivors. It is why this is not a story to be read with caution, for I will begin it with its ending.

This is the journey of a survivor.
This is a fight for life which was won and is still being lived.
Yes, it is ongoing, but our protagonist has fought her way out of the hardest part.
Her chapters are still being written, but her demons are no longer their focus.

Chapter 1

My friend, Jane.

This is a story about a girl.

Her name is Jane and, for what felt like a small piece of forever, she forgot what living was.

* * *

Once upon a time, Jane was a very happy little girl.

She had two parents who loved her very much – probably too much – and a sister and a brother, Rosie and Alex, who were also her best friends. They lived in a semi-detached house in a small English village with a Magnolia tree in the garden that painted the lawn cream and fuchsia twice a year. Jane learned to play the piano on Tuesdays, white skin and black hair matching the ivory keys she tapped upon in a rhythm entirely of her own creation. She played hockey on Saturdays and awoke, stiff and sore, on Sunday mornings with bruised knees and elbows - all that remained of her valiant attempts to tackle, drive and score.

She had a childhood that was perfect.

No one died. No one abused her. No one called her fat or made fun of the mole on the left side of her chin (except her Grandad, who called it a 'coco-pop'). She cycled beside her parents on their Sunday morning runs and she made playdough out of flour and salt when her siblings' friends came over for tea. She worked hard at school and was her own worst critic, but her mother and father reminded her that, no matter what, they were proud of the person she was – not what she achieved – and that was that. She played every sport and acted in all kinds of plays. She went to concerts with friends and got tipsy after one WKD. She learnt to drive in a bright green Vauxhall Agila that she nicknamed 'The Hulk' and she passed her test second time around after losing control of the windscreen wipers on the first. She had her first kiss with a drunk sixteen-year-old at their "after prom" party in 2012 and thought she was in love. She fell in love with a boy, eighteen months later, with whom she never thought she could. She ran around reservoirs and it made her feel alive. She painted with her fingertips and it reminded her that she was. She was content in her body. It did exactly what she needed it to until, all of a sudden, it didn't, and then this picture-perfect life she led came tumbling down around her.

Jane became a jigsaw of a girl. Scattered on the floor.

This is the story of how that jumbled mess of disjointed pieces found its whole again.
It is honest and it is raw, for these are the confessions of a fractured soul.

The confessions of my friend, Jane.

It is a song whose rhythm and cadence are still being harmonised, jilted and jarring at times. It is one that is capable of both the greatest crescendos and the faintest, most delicate melodies. It is unfiltered and rough around the edges, but it is a battle that celebrates the importance of hope, even when all seemed utterly hopeless.

Chapter 2
13 months, 24 pounds

In September 2012, Jane started Sixth Form College at her old secondary school. One of the really popular girls had lost a significant amount of weight and Jane thought she looked good. Everyone couldn't stop talking about her. They kept saying, 'Joanna's anorexic', 'look at her hands'. Joanna's fingers were like pencils, bony and tiny and blue and cold, even though it was mid-summer. She wore a scarf and a vest and every time she took it off to get changed before P.E., the whole room went silent as the other girls turned and saw every single rib xylophone its way along her spine. Jane wanted to be so small that her ribcage jutted out like Joanna's and her face was just as angular. Jane had a "love heart" shaped face. Mum reminded her of it every time Jane complained about her "chubby cheeks". Jane hated it. She wanted to be as delicate and petite as Joanna. Jane thought 'I want to be anorexic', but what she meant was 'I want to be skinny'. She did not know what "anorexic" meant and, if she had, she wouldn't have wished it on anyone, especially not herself.

In October 2012, Jane walked into her A-Level History class and the boy who had been her prom date that summer, Toby, came and sat in front of her. He was her first kiss and she had been a flustery mess of blushing embarrassment around him ever since they first met when they were fourteen. His ego got a boost from her nervous bumblings whenever he would smile or wink at her. He was one of the popular pupils, like Joanna, and Jane remembered how the two of them – Toby and Joanna - had flirted on the GCSE Battlefields trip the previous year. She had stood nervously on the side-lines, wishing it were her instead. She thought to herself, 'I will be skinny' because Joanna was skinny and, maybe if she was skinny, Toby might fancy her too.

There was another girl in that class; she was called Amara. Amara was a year older than Jane, but had to redo the year because she was anorexic.

Amara's fingers were even bluer than Joanna's and when she stood up to shrug her blazer on as they left the class, Jane saw her hip bones spiking through her skirt. Her legs were thin and spindly. Like twigs. Once upon a time, they had both held the school records for 1500m and cross country. Jane had competed in cross country with Amara and she was quick – a lot quicker than Jane – but now Amara was not allowed to do sports anymore, she was too underweight.

They had a cake rota on Fridays, but Amara never ate the cakes; she only brought them in. After a couple of weeks, Jane stopped eating the cakes made on Fridays for the cake rota too. If Amara could resist, why couldn't she?

In November 2012, Jane started going to parties and drinking alcohol. There was a big gathering after the Sixth Form Christmas dinner. Jane drank a lot and so did Toby. He kissed her behind a curtain. It made her stomach somersault and her chest tingle. She felt special. She had lost a little weight by this time. She thought that maybe that was why he kissed her, that maybe now he would want to be with her. She was wrong. A couple of weeks later, Toby got a girlfriend. Jane found her on Instagram after he posted a photo of them together. She had amazing cheekbones and was really skinny. Jane thought she was anorexic, everyone seemed to be nowadays. She wanted to be anorexic too, if it meant boys would find her more attractive. Jane still had not grasped what "anorexic" meant.

In December 2012, Jane got a membership to the fancy gym that Toby and his friend, Zak, went to. Zak had joined Sixth Form in September. Jane thought that he had the most beautiful brown eyes. They were the sort of brown that changed colour when the sunlight hit them differently. His skin was the colour of caramel and, when he smiled, it was the kind of smile that could light up a room.

Jane's friend, Maria, also started the "12 days of Christmas" trial at the fancy gym at the same time. She had arms that were so skinny you could fit your forefinger and thumb around them. Jane wanted arms that small, but she had bigger arms from rowing and hockey.

Jane was strong. Maria was anorexic. Anorexic like Joanna and Amara and Toby's girlfriend. Maria was weak. She couldn't lift the weights like Jane could. Jane began to associate "strong" with "fat". She just wanted to be small. Instead of wanting to be anorexic, Jane needed to be. It became her preoccupying thought. An obsession.

In January 2013, the worst year of Jane's life began.

Mum started getting concerned that Jane wasn't eating much and was exercising a lot more than she used to. She cried after Christmas dinner, having watched Jane push potatoes around her plate saying she wasn't hungry. Jane gave Alex the chocolate from her stocking and announced that she wasn't 'a fan' of trifle and cream and custard anymore. Every Christmas, without fail, Jane had gone for seconds, sometimes even thirds – they all did, they were big eaters in their family – but this year, Jane barely finished her first plate. A plate that was absent of any real carbohydrates or fats.

Mum told Dad she was worried and they sat her down after school one night when her sister and her brother were at sports practice. They told her that they were afraid she was over-working herself and eating too little. They reminded her that, no matter what, they were proud of her, but Jane was adamant she was fine.

Toby had stopped spending time with Jane since the new girlfriend and Jane felt lonely. She started returning the flirty chit-chat that Zak had been throwing her way since September. She just wanted to feel wanted and Zak made her feel that way.

In February, 2013, Jane's dog, Katie, died. Jane and Mum watched Katie get put down. When they came home, Jane made Mum pasta because Mum was still paralysed by the shock of it all. Jane ate a little because she wanted Mum to feel better. It was the first time she had eaten pasta since the summer. Pasta was one of the first things she cut out. She hadn't seen Mum cry like that before. It broke her heart and she knew that eating something would make Mum a little less worried. Jane loved her Mum more than she loved the feeling of hunger gnawing in her belly and she hadn't eaten all day so she didn't mind as much. Mum's tears replaced the empty silence that echoed in the absence of Katie's padding tail. Sobs instead of skittering paws. But they were not temporary. No, crying would no longer be an oddity in their little semi-detached home. In fact, it would soon become normality.

In March, 2013, Jane's periods stopped. Mum asked her when she had last had one. Jane lied. Mum didn't believe her. She made an appointment

with the GP. The doctor weighed Jane, but Jane didn't want to know her weight. Mum sat there the whole time and did a lot of talking. She knew her daughter wasn't very well but the doctor said Jane's weight was within the healthy BMI range. He recommended that she 'eat a burger every now and then' and she would be fine.
They left the doctors' surgery.
In Jane's eyes, she had failed. She was still a "healthy" weight and "healthy", just like "strong", now meant "fat".

Jane swore never to eat a burger again.

In April, 2013, Jane turned seventeen. She started learning how to drive. She also started using the Sixth Form gym now that hockey season was over. She would go every day after school and would also run when she was at home. She started lying about what she had eaten at college and watched Joanna pick the batter off her fish on Fridays. The tiniest scraps of white cod were all that made it to her mouth as she shivered in her ever-growing jumper-skin. Jane's lunch was now soup or salad. The steaming bowl of apple crumble - her favourite for as long as she could remember - lay cold and untouched at the side of her tray.

Amara was no longer in school. Apparently, she had had a "relapse". Jane didn't know what this meant. She just assumed that Amara had stopped eating again and that she would be back before the end of the term, once the problem was resolved.

Jane started to feel tired all of the time. It made her fratchety and grumpy and put a strain on the relationships she had with her family. She refused to eat with them and, when Mum begged her to because she could see that Jane was losing weight, Jane repeated the words of the GP over and over in a mantra of irreverence. She was "healthy". She just needed to eat the occasional burger, remember?

In May, 2013, Jane went on study leave for her AS Levels. This meant that she had complete freedom over her food and exercise. No-one was around and able to monitor her eating. The lying became second nature.

She was exhausted. Balancing exams, post-exam workouts, revision and food restriction was draining. She could barely keep her eyes open, never mind focus on the questions, formulae and words that blurred in smears across the exam papers slapped on the desk in front of her.

Mum and Dad took it in turns to take her out in the car now that she was competent enough to drive without a professional instructor. Jane started to find it hard to focus on the road ahead and her vision occasionally went a little blurry. On one particularly bad occasion, she forgot to look left as she pulled out of a junction and a truck nearly killed her and Dad. Dad yelled, as was his every right, but Jane felt numb. She didn't have the energy to argue back. Her body had exhausted itself in the rush of adrenaline that had ricocheted through her. She used to prefer driving with Dad, but now all he seemed to talk about was her eating.

One afternoon, they drove to the big Asda down by Tufford lane and he told her to pull into the garage so that they could get petrol. When he came back, he had two Cadbury Wispa bars with him.

Jane felt sick.

Dad made Jane feel so guilty with the words he was saying – words about her breaking Mum's heart and words about how selfish her actions were - that she ate the chocolate bar. Jane was hysterical as she drove home. Dad kept saying how proud he was of her.

Jane felt grotesque.

An Extract from Jane's Diary
May 2013

Just had another panic
Feel so sad
Dad's pissing me off with the numbers he keeps throwing at me;
I'm just so scared
I need my Mummy all the time;
She made me eat more fish so now I feel fat and sick but then when I tried to put my tissue in the bin she took the fish out and fed it to me and now I want to cry.
I like the bathroom.
It's cold in the bath when I feel warm with hate.
I don't like the hate.
It makes me feel dirty and alone and hot.
But my sister tried to help;
All I want is not to be scared all the time.
Please God help me.

In June, 2013, Mum made another appointment with the GP. Jane made Mum wait outside till the doctor had weighed her this time. He told Jane that she had lost weight. Jane felt good. She opened the door and told Mum she could come back in. The doctor wrote a note recommending that Jane see a child psychologist provided by the NHS and said that Mum and Dad should keep track of her weight. Jane agreed, but only so that she could secretly monitor her weight loss herself. Whilst they waited for the appointment with the psychologist, Mum and Dad weighed Jane every week and wrote her weight down on a chart scrawled on the back of the cardboard from a cereal packet that they blue-tacked to the back of the kitchen cupboard door. Jane felt sick every morning of a weigh day. She would stand naked on the scale and close her eyes. Dad would wait with baited breath behind the bathroom door and Mum looked at the fluttering digits as they said what she already knew; what she could see so plainly in the pale canary of a daughter that perched before her. With Mum's sigh and the steady stream of tears at the ever-dropping figures, Jane's chest felt a wave of relief.

The grumble in her tummy reminded her she was succeeding. Hunger pangs became the most delicious of sensations. They provided her with the greatest satisfaction and she began to forget what it was like to entertain thoughts that did not revolve around eating or exercising. Her preoccupation was the plummeting of her BMI. It made her feel powerful and she wore it on her skin like a perfume - the perfume of inevitable decline.

In July, 2013, Jane met with the child psychologist. She told him everything, well, almost. She told him how she felt fat compared to the other girls. She explained how she wanted to lose weight, but that Mum and Dad wouldn't let her. She told him how they were weighing her every week and that she hated it, that it made her feel even worse about herself. He asked her why she wanted to lose weight. She told him 'because I want to be skinny'.

He asked her what her grades were like, whether she was a "perfectionist" and was she ever bullied at school? Did she have a boyfriend and what did she want to do after her A-Levels? So many questions which didn't seem relevant, but that Jane answered as robotically and "honestly" as she could. She kept looking at the vegetable patch outside the window. The psychologist told her he would write to her family with a suggested plan of action and Jane thanked him as she left. He wasn't very helpful. She didn't think he would be.

The recommendation with his proposed course of action arrived a week later in the post. The letter was addressed to Jane and her parents. It stated that Jane was a "healthy" teenage girl who simply struggled with low self-esteem and negative body-image. It suggested that her parents were too controlling and that they should take a step back from their constant observation of their daughter, including the weekly monitoring of her weight. This was not necessary, according to the psychologist, and Jane should be left alone. Mum and Dad did not like this. Jane loved it – with the exception of the statement that she was "healthy". No, that was a failure.

 She had been at it for ten months now, so why wasn't her BMI reflecting that? What she couldn't comprehend was that muscle weighs more than fat. As an athlete, her body fat percentage was plummeting but, as her muscles continued to strain and stretch and work themselves into the ground, they got "heavier". Muscle and fat ratios are not features that BMI measurements take into account. Therefore, in Jane's eyes, she was still "healthy". She decided that it was time to take a more drastic course of action.

An Extract from Jane's Diary
July 2013

I wish everyone would leave me the fuck alone.
I want to cry and sometimes I just think life is so **HARD**

Please God
give me strength.
Please God give
me strength.
Please God give me
strength.
Please God give me strength.
Please God give me strength.
Please God give me strength.
Please God give me strength.
Please God give me strength.
Please God give me strength.

In August, 2013, the weekly weigh-ins at home stopped. Jane no longer had to face the shame of the scales every week. Instead, she faced her reflection. It was a silhouette which, to everyone else, was getting progressively thinner – a sharp-edged and jagged frame of a girl, the soft curves of a maturing young woman replaced by bone. She did not see what her family and her friends saw. Their comments 'you've lost a lot of weight, Jane. Are you eating properly?' failed to give her any sense of joy – she assumed they were simply lying.

On the family trip to France, she had her first mental breakdown. They had had traybake for dinner and she had refused to eat the potato, or the chorizo, or the chicken. Her uncle had made pancakes for dessert. She had not expected it and her fear was paralysing. After everyone had eaten, she ran upstairs and began hyperventilating and shaking and hysterically rocking until her sister, Rosie, opened the door and found her semi-naked underneath the sheets. Rosie found Mum and told her to go upstairs. Mum took Jane for a walk. She told Jane how worried she was. Jane told Mum everything that was bubbling inside of her head, how she thought that she was fat and how she hated the 'rolls' that bunched up around her tummy. That her thighs were "thunder thighs" and her face was round and chubby – she felt so ugly. Mum told her that she was beautiful, but Jane didn't hear her – she was too caught up in the tangles and knots of self-hatred and loathing that anorexia was weaving inside of her head.

They went to Lourdes and Jane went to Confession. She told the priest that she was worried and that she knew she needed to stop because she was hurting her family. He listened and told her that it would be OK and to use that love for her family to get back on track. After Confession, they went to be "bathed" in the Holy spring. For a while this "cleansing" made Jane feel a little better, but then the voice returned and she found herself chewing up food and spitting it into napkins before hiding them underneath the rubbish in the bin again.

On their twenty-five-hour drive back from France, Mum and Dad weighed Jane at Granny Sally's house where they stopped for a break. Jane had lost a significant amount of weight. It made Jane feel lots of different things. She felt sick because of the way Mum and Dad reacted, their tanned faces suddenly white with a fear that had been almost forgotten amidst the play-pretend of "happy-families-on-their-summer-holiday". She felt relieved that all those un-weighed portions and the candyfloss she had allowed herself to indulge in (once) as they wandered around French marketplaces had not caused her to "pile on the pounds", as she had so greatly feared. She felt proud, that finally, all of the effort and the exhaustion and the tears and the incessant growling of hunger pangs in her belly – yawning good morning and grumbling good night – were starting to pay off.

Sick. Relieved. Proud.
She examined her body as she stood and stared at her reflection in the dim
flickering light of Granny's bathroom. The tortoiseshell bathtub reflected the
blue of her fingertips and the shape of her ribcage was now kissed olive
with the rays of the Mediterranean sun. This was anorexia's first concrete
victory and Jane found herself addicted to the thrill.

At the end of August, Jane went to a party after work. Zak was there. They
sat beside the firepit and he kissed her and they decided that they would
be boyfriend and girlfriend. This was the third time that Jane had ever been
kissed. The first time, 'Human' by The Killers, had been playing. This time,
instead of focusing on the music, she focused on the person. Zak would be
the first boy that she would ever love, but he would also be the first heart
that she would ever break.

In September, 2013, Mum made another appointment at the doctor's, but
this time she requested a female doctor. Jane went into the appointment,
as did Mum. She refused to stay outside, as Jane was technically still "a
child". The doctor weighed Jane and Mum told her that Jane's periods had
stopped. The doctor took Jane's blood pressure and heart rate, all the while
nodding her head, as Mum cried and told her how she felt useless because
the psychologist had recommended that she and Dad leave Jane alone
and now Jane wasn't really Jane anymore and it was all her fault. Jane
cried too and tried to tell Mum that it wasn't her fault but her words weren't
really making any sense and it all just sounded like one insincere mumble.
The doctor looked at Mum, dead in the eye, and Jane felt the chill of the
room grow ever more palpable as pity filled the silence. The doctor said
she would be referring Jane to CAMHS – Child and Adolescent Mental
Health Services - and that she should expect to hear from them soon.

They left the doctors' and sat in the car. Mum held Jane's hand and told
her that they were going to help her get better. Jane squeezed it back and
nodded, but was terrified. She didn't need to get better. She didn't want to
get better. If she was going to be monitored more regularly, if they were
going to force her to gain weight, she needed to up her game. She needed
to accelerate the weight loss before they began supervising her more
closely.

Zak was not told about any of this.

Jane's mood used to change, almost unrecognisably, in the minutes prior to him picking her up in his little white car. She tried to pretend she was a normal seventeen-year-old as she opened the front door and he kissed her gently on the doorstep. He didn't know about the hysterics and the piles of clothes that lay strewn across her bedroom floor as she emptied her wardrobe, trying to find something she didn't hate herself in prior to his arrival. He didn't need to know. They would drive around for hours listening to The Lumineers or Drake – depending on where the mood would take them - and he would hold her hand as she rested her head against the window whilst he steered with the other. When she was with him, she wasn't thinking about food or exercise. He was her calm and her escapism and, as the absence of any love she had for herself grew exponentially, it morphed into an unfamiliar, blooming sensation in her chest whenever she thought of him.

Jane fell in love with Zak. Anorexia took her from him.

In October, 2013, Jane started attending the outpatient clinic. She had a dietician, a psychiatrist, a nurse who took her weekly observations and another, "key" nurse, who explained all the various appointments she had to go to and talked to her about the things that the psychiatrist did not. She didn't like any of them. They were all trying to make her fat. Or so she thought. The dietician gave her meal plans that she absolutely refused to follow. The tuna sandwich she was meant to have for lunch at college became a half and then a quarter and then a single bite. A bite which she would hold in her mouth till she could sprint out of the dining hall and spit it into the toilet. On one occasion, her maths teacher caught her mid-bolt and she was forced to swallow the warm tuna smush so that she could answer his question.

That was a bad day.

Dad was a teacher at her school and when he was on lunch duty, he would watch her in the dining hall. This meant that Jane had to develop habits and behaviours that would fool him into thinking she was abiding by her prescribed meal plan. Behaviours and habits that were steeped in deceit. One of the easiest ways she could get around eating was by promising that the little sandwich bags of counted Minstrels he would lovingly make up for her every day as her prescribed "mid-morning snack", were being eaten at breaktimes. In reality, they were thrown in the big green bin outside the lockers as soon as Dad headed up to his classroom. To fill the void in her stomach, Jane drank pint after pint of green tea and Pepsi Max. To fill the time she should have spent eating – "lunch" time - she walked around the town with Zak, feeding the ducks porridge oats and occasionally stopping by the river for a quick kiss in the autumn sunshine.

Jane's weight did not go up. In fact, it kept dropping. Every week, without fail, the digits would flicker further and further down. Eventually, the psychiatrist requested that Jane come in twice a week, rather than weekly. It was on one of these secondary visits that Jane's heart rate plummeted to less than half of what it should have been. The day Jane was due to take her driving test. Instead, on Friday the 25th October, she found herself lying in a hospital gown amongst a tangle of cables listening to the zipzipzip of yellow paper as it curled out of the ECG printer. Twenty-four pounds lighter than she had been thirteen months earlier.

Chapter 3
Postman Pat and his Black and White Cat

Harry Potter was one of Jane's very first childhood friends.

She read the first book when she was five years old and everyone at the nursery couldn't believe how literate and eloquent such a young child could be. Her imagination was always active and she spent her primary school years with her nose in a book and fingers in paint pots. She made up for the lack of friends she had in the real world by conjuring up her own playmates right out of her head or from the pages she thumbed with sticky, eager fingers. She spent her early years adventuring with 'Willum', 'Gillum' and 'Pilum' but, as she was gifted with the art of reading, her universe became exponentially more exciting. The landscape of her mind was shared with the likes of Harry, Hermione and Ron. It was only when her siblings came along that slowly those paper comrades faded into an exclusively imagined world and she was able to share her escapades with Rosie and Alex in a world she could see, taste, hear, smell and touch.

The years she spent as a child were precious.

They were simpler times and she was not responsible for her wellbeing or, to some extent, her actions. One day, her parents picked her up and put her down for the last time. One day, Jane picked up a fork and popped food into her mouth of her own accord and no one would feed her again. One day she went to her wardrobe and she pulled out a t-shirt and some shorts and she tugged them over scabby knees and scuffed elbows herself and, in that uncoordinated and hair-tangling action, she was no longer dependent on the hands of another to nourish her or clean her or clothe her. She developed points of independence within her umbrella of wholly dependent existence.

Mum did not ever pause to think about the last time she did any of these things because, at the time, she didn't know that it was the final time. Most parents do not – that is the bittersweet fact of life. However, where - for the majority of healthy children - all of these last times usually happen between the ages of two and four, Jane's last time was aged seventeen.

Let me rephrase that.

One day, her parents picked her up and put her down for the last time,
 or so they thought.
One day, Jane picked up a fork and popped food into her mouth of her own accord and no one would feed her again,
or so she thought.
One day she went to her wardrobe and she pulled out a t-shirt and some shorts and she tugged them over scabby knees and scuffed elbows herself and, in that uncoordinated and hair-tangling action, she was no longer dependent on the hands of another to nourish her or clean her or clothe her. She developed points of independence within her umbrella of wholly dependent existence –
until anorexia blew her independence away and those hands that had so lovingly nurtured her came gently back to guide and aid.

 Mothers never forget how to be a Mum.

Mum never thought she would spoon feed her child again. She never thought she would spend the night in a paediatric ward, huddled close to her daughter to keep her warm. She never thought that she would become her child's sole means of movement and the thought of having to wash her child's hair and towel dry her body was not ever one that crossed her mind after the age of five. Mum was forty-five when, instead of having three teenage children, she found herself with a toddler, a seventeen-year-old toddler. A toddler who was capable of self-harm, a toddler with ten A*s at GCSE, a toddler who was on the verge of passing her driving test and a toddler who had a boyfriend with a car. A toddler with pictures from her Fifth Year Prom. A toddler who had offers from two universities to study English Literature. A toddler that needed twenty-four-seven supervision for fear her heart may stop beating.

Anorexia had turned a perfectly normal, perfectly functioning human being, into the most vulnerable and prepubescent version of herself. Jane wanted to be skinny. She wanted to be small.

Jane did not just become "small" in the sense of size. She became small and helpless. She became vulnerable and dependent. In striving for control, she lost it and, on the 25th of October, 2013, the reality of the consequences of what she was doing hit her. The stark and brutal awakening of being admitted to a paediatric ward at the age of seventeen. Something which occurred, ultimately, as a result of her own hand.

After Jane's ECG results came back, it became clear that her vital organs were starting to feel the effects of her self-induced starvation. Simply put, her body had begun shutting itself down.

Jane's most pressing problem was no longer the state of her mental health, it was her corporeal decline and, due to the rapid deterioration of her psychological state over the last few weeks, her weight had fallen into a bracket which required a strict "refeeding" program, one the consultant hoped an intensive week-long stint in the paediatric ward would kickstart.

On admission to the ward, the consultant took Jane and her family – all five of them – into the day-room. It was a small square box of a thing with an old TV set and some scratchy blue sofas. Her statistics were scribbled on a chart that perched on the doctor's knee. Jane noticed the start of a ladder running up the left-hand side of the doctor's tights and she followed the trail with tired eyes as words like 'amber zone', 'anorexic' and 'shutdown' echoed out amidst the monotony of Dr Rolling's voice. Mum squeezed Jane's hand and Jane pressed back. Dad put his arm around her and said 'I'm so sorry' but she pulled away, shaking off his embrace with cold indifference. It wasn't Dad's fault. He didn't understand – he thought she was choosing not to eat, which was true, but what he didn't understand, was the reality that this wasn't a "diet" or some silly "fad", as he coined it. No, this was an illness – a disease – and Jane had about as much control over her thoughts and actions as a patient with a broken arm has over deciding the rate at which the splinters in their busted bone begin to heal themselves.

Jane could hear what the adults were saying, but she couldn't seem to process it. Her glance shifted from the ladder in the consultant's tights to the corner of the room where she could see her brother and sister, silently crying. Rosie held Alex's hand. They didn't know what an eating disorder was - all they could see was a stranger who had once been their big sister, now hunched over and shivering, sobbing into the scruffy cable knit of her jumper.

Where was the girl who had chased them around the garden with a water gun on warm summer evenings?
Where was the girl who had pretended to be a Cyberman and hunted them into Mum's wardrobe when they occupied the 'Land of the Make Believe'?
Where was their babysitter?
Where was the person they had come to for help with particularly tricky piano pieces?
Where had she gone?
This was not Jane.
Jane would have stood up and told the doctor that this was all a big mistake, that she was fine!
Look!
She was strong and fast and happy!
Jane didn't need to be pushed around in a wheelchair! She was the new record holder for the school 1500m.
She wasn't old and crumbly and dependent on a squeaky chair to get her from A to B!
She was strong! She was feisty! She was Jane!

Jane wished she could reach over and hug them. She wished she could tell them that they were right, that this wasn't Jane and that sooner or later the skinny twig of a thing that had taken over their sister's body would be cast away – far, far, far away - and that she would be back, driving them to school and singing along to George Ezra on the radio in no time. Unfortunately, as the nurse knocked on the door and opened it wide enough to roll Jane's newest accessory into the midst of the palpable heartbreak, all she could do was muster the slightest of weary smiles. She looked at the two of them and she tried to say all that she could in that single glance. A look that bounced between six, brimming, chestnut pools.

As she pulled herself up and sat down for the first time in the wheelchair, the reality of the singular naive thought she had had back in October, 2012, hit her, 'I want to be anorexic'.

If this was anorexia, anorexia was not what she wanted.

Even as she sobbed down the phone to her aunty and told her the prognosis, even as she felt Mum's tears bounce off the top of her head as she pushed her down the corridor to Ward 27, even as the consultant's words reverberated sharply through her conscious mind - 'anorexic', 'amber zone', 'shutdown'- all Jane could feel was fear.

But, it was not fear for her life, which she had now been told was unquestionably at high risk. It was not fear for her future, which was now resolutely on hold, with no prospect of returning to Sixth Form after October half term. It was not fear of the reality that she was now dependent on a wheelchair with one-to-one observation every time she took a shower or went to the toilet in case she would make herself sick or exercise whilst momentarily alone.

No. Her heart filled with the fear of loss of control.

In hospital she was under constant supervision. She could not exercise the deceitful habits she had picked up whilst at home. She was not the master of her day-to-day actions and she was not ventriloquising her future. She was a child, in every sense of the word, and these dependencies - these regressions - were only going to get exponentially worse.

In times such as these, when happiness was as unfamiliar a concept to Jane as the enjoyment of food, it was not as simple as fumbling for a light switch in a darkened room. Jane needed help, a flashlight to aid her blind panic and, for a while, she thought that this might come from God.

Jane hoped that God would answer the prayers for survival said in her more lucid states - even though they were few and far between. She asked the priest to bring her the Holy Communion when she was on bedrest in the paediatric wing and she kept her rosary beads and St Christopher nestled in the cavity that her jutting collarbones and sternum now formed.

An Extract from Jane's Diary
October 2013

I want to live with Grandma
I can't do it anymore.
Please God
give me

strength.
Please God
give me
strength.
Please God
give me
strength.
Please God
give me
strength.
Everyone just leave me alone
please
I'm still feeling
Fucking terrible
Please help me stop feeling like this
I can't do it anymore.
I want to just be by myself
And NO-ONE
will watch me and no one will care and life will be fine again like it used to
be when I had freedom.

But there was nothing anyone could do to save her. The only person who
could do that, was Jane.

For a week Jane's parents came to visit her every day. They would arrive
early in the morning, in time for Mum to sit with her and watch her eat
her breakfast. Then they would take her around the hospital corridors in
her wheelchair so that she could get a change of scenery from the garish
cartoons that peppered the walls of the ward. After two or three laps of the
hospital, Dad would take Rosie and Alex to the little café by the shop in
reception for their lunch, while Mum stayed and tried to help Jane eat hers.
Each mealtime was announced with the Postman Pat theme tune, a sound
which sent a chill running down Jane's spine, chased back by a wave of
nausea rising in her stomach. This was not a specialist eating disorder ward
and the nurses did not have time to stay and watch Jane while she ate - this
was down to Mum.

Mum would sit on the edge of the bed for forty minutes or so, every
time. On mornings, she would desperately attempt to get her daughter
to eat the soggy white triangles of toast that lay cold and fingered on the
tray in front of her and, in evenings, it was flakes of stinking mackerel.

Unsurprisingly, this unappetising platter of Jane's most "taboo" food groups - carbohydrates and fats - eventually led to her first ever nutritional supplement, Fortisip.

Fortisip is a thick, gloopy drink made for people who struggle to consume enough solid food to maintain a balanced diet. It is used to help treat people with eating disorders who cannot bear to digest solid food because, in the case of Jane, the act of putting solid food in her mouth was too much guilt for her to bear. With Fortisip, there was no question about the exact number of calories, whereas, all other food was just a rough approximation.

Jane knew the number of calories in everything;
An egg – 66; the white – 17
A banana – 88 per100g
Honey – 44 per spoon
Almond milk (unsweetened) -11-16 per 100ml
Low fat Natural Yoghurt – 66 per 100g
...the list goes on.

One evening, on day two or three, she decided that she would completely refuse to so much as touch the food hastily heaped onto the tray in front of her. Usually, she would push it around the plate and gag a little in disgust, but tonight, even picking up the fork was deemed a failure in anorexia's eyes. That night, the spiral shifted to a darker place.

Mum was there, as was now part of their "normal" routine, and she had just rolled Jane back from her daily shower. Mum had to stand and watch as Jane undressed, her ribcage jutting out like empty coat hangers on a rack. From the base of her spine all the way up to the nape of her neck, bloomed the deep indigo smudge of bruised ivory. Despite the hospital bed being soft, her bones pressed hard against the surface of her skin. The soft Laguna down that brushed her arms and stomach - famine's very own fur - caught the breath in Mum's throat. Every time she pulled the orange cardigan off her daughter's frame, she felt her heartbeat quicken and hastily gulped back the aching sob of a heartache which now seemed omnipresent.

Jane had regressed into the body of a child.

The soft lumps that had grown on her chest, snugly fitting into the AAA cup of a Marks and Spencer's sports bra, were now gone. Her arms struggled to lift the hospital duvet when she settled down to sleep at night and the gap between her legs seemed impossibly wide. The bruises on her back crept in ivy fronds all the way along her shins, forearms and hips – anything that possessed a corner or an edge had the power to fracture this delicate skeleton of a woman.

Her face was gaunt and angular.

When she stared, with hollow black eyes, at the child who stood in the mirror in front of her - a cold shadow of a human, empty and brittle - the lines around her mouth brought her comfort. They were a sign that even the fat stores in her cheeks had been sacrificed in her body's desperate attempt to cling on to life. When a person starves themselves to the extent that Jane did, their body goes into survival mode. Eventually, after a long enough period without sufficient nutrition, it starts to digest the muscle that makes up the vital organs, for example, the heart.

Mum tucked Jane up in bed and held her hand - as she did every time the little food trolley came along the corridor. She sat and tried to encourage her to eat the meal that was her "medicine".

Jane refused, Mum cajoled.
Jane refused, Mum begged.

Jane kept refusing until the only option left was the Fortisip. The dietician had threatened her with it for the past three days but tonight was the first time Jane hadn't put a single morsel in her mouth which meant, there was no alternative. Part of her was intrigued because the girl who lay in the bed opposite her had been drinking the supplements for the majority of the time Jane had been there. She was struggling with anorexia, amongst other things, but was a lot further down the line than Jane. Her liver had begun to fail and she was waiting for a kidney transplant. The girl must have only been sixteen or seventeen. She told Jane that no matter what, she must never, ever be forced to resort to the Nasogastric Tube because, from there, there was no going back. Any control, and by that she really meant any, was lost when the Fortisip was pumped into the body via a plastic tube. Though Jane's mind was lost in a place absent of hope or lucidity, she knew that resorting to the tube would kill her parents.

This was not a step she was willing to take.
Jane loved her mother with a fierce intensity that meant the heartbreak she felt as she watched Mum desperately begging her to eat, superseded the fear of the Fortisip. Guilt for her mother's pain motivated her to momentarily forget her fear of food. Just as it had done the day that Katie died. She was too tired to fight against Mum after a day of arguing over every single mouthful. So, she sat with the little yellow bottle in front of her and Mum pulled the straw out of the packaging, puncturing the tin foil disc that covered the top with a gentle Pop!

Fortisip was not food.

Mum repeated it over and over. She told Jane that it was what Grandad had to drink because he was bed-ridden and couldn't swallow anything remotely solid. By thinking about it as medicine, it made it slightly easier for Jane, not to ingest, but to rationalise. Drinking the supplement wasn't "eating", it was medicinal. They were calories, yes, and they were in a bottle that tasted like a poorly mixed banana milkshake, yes, but they were calories so concentrated that Jane could drink 250ml of fluid and not have to battle with the sensation of a tummy full of solid food – an unfamiliar sensation now that hunger pains filled the absent space.

Food was the only way she would get better and, despite it being repeated to her, every day and every mealtime again and again and again, she refused to believe it.

She couldn't.

It was the bittersweet irony of Jane's eating disorder. The thing that would save her was the thing she feared the most. The only way she would be able to rationalise eating as normal was by regaining complete cognitive function; to possess comprehensive clarity of thought and judgement, something which required sufficient nutrition.

Rationalisation was crucial in order for her to understand why food was essential to living, but rationalisation could only come with a well-nourished mind;

A starved body = a starved mind
A starved mind = an inability to rationalise

Food would provide Jane with the ability to see reason but for an eating disorder sufferer;

Food = The Enemy

despite

Food = The Cure.

Jane placed the bottle to her lips and she tentatively sipped. She was shocked because it did not taste as bad as she thought it would. She felt guilty but it was a new type of guilt, one she had not felt before.

It stemmed from an unfamiliar feeling;

pleasure.

Jane found herself almost enjoying the drink. It horrified her. The sweet artificial banana reminded her of the yellow milkshakes they used to get from McDonalds when they were kids. The "luxury" addition to their Happy Meals that they would nervously ask Dad for because they knew it cost a little bit more than a Fanta. Jane hadn't eaten fast food for about three years – she had grown out of its appeal when she hit thirteen after someone told her that it made children turn the colour blue. It was an association she had struggled to ignore ever since and, if she did go to a Drive Through, even before the anorexia, she would stick to liquids rather than solids.

As Jane remembered those early days, she lost herself in the nostalgia and, by the time she found herself back in the present, the bottle was nearly empty. For so long, nothing of any real creamy-ness or "indulgence" had passed her lips and, all of a sudden, there it was, sliding its way up the straw into her mouth. She couldn't stop herself drinking. She hated every morsel of her being but she couldn't seem to stop.

Anorexia was in shock and, in the voice's momentary paralysis, Jane supped.

But then the moment ended and Jane put the bottle down. She was fraught and anxious and frustrated for she was trapped in a body that she had no control over – whether it be the speed of her weight loss, independence of movement or, now, ability to control her feelings about flavour and texture. For months she had taught herself that food absolutely could not be liked.

It was the adversary and she must despise it at all costs. She knew that she must teach herself to dislike the taste of the Fortisip. As long as she secretly enjoyed it, she would continue to be the fat failure that anorexia tormented her with.

* * *

The day Jane drank her first Fortisip was not a good day for Jane's mental health. It did, however, prove one thing to Mum. Her daughter was capable of letting an emotion stronger than guilt dictate her actions. And that emotion? That emotion was love.

Even if the love she felt was immediately replaced by self-hatred the moment that the straw sucked empty air bubbles. Even if it was as fleeting as the pop! of the straw through the tinfoil lid. It was a day that marked the beginning of a new type of dependence, a reliance on supplements over solids and, for the next two months, Jane's consumption of solid foods lessened progressively until, one day, her entire daily intake was the colour of tepid milk. The stench on her breath got stronger as the supplement intake got higher.

She smelt like she was dying.

At the end of the week Jane spent in the paediatric ward, she was wheeled out into the car park, two boxes of Fortisip resting on her knees. She had been discharged with strict instructions for bed rest and constant observation until her weight stabilised and she began to move her way up the "zones" from amber, to green and eventually, gold.

Jane had no intention of doing this.
*Anorexia had no intention of letting Jane do this.

As she collapsed into the back seat of the car, she was already planning how she would go about losing the pitiful grams she had gained whilst in the paediatric wing. Her rosary beads remained in a discarded heap on the empty hospital bed and, in their place, Jane's new crutch, the wheelchair, was folded and wedged into the boot behind her. Jane thought that anorexia was the voice of reason. What she failed to understand was that, in promising her the golden gift of being "thin", anorexia wasn't saving her, it was killing her.

Chapter 4

Zak

The period following Jane's stint in the inpatient unit was a month steeped in darkness. Winter brought with it shorter days and longer nights and Jane's own blackness became impenetrable. In "taking control" of her eating, Jane lost control of absolutely everything else. She lost the essence of who she was and her actions left scars that were not only formative in her later notions of identity, but also the identities of those who loved her the most.

The next five weeks of Jane's life were a blur.

In a severely malnourished brain, a person's processing skills become drastically reduced and they have to stop doing everyday things like driving or working because of the impact that starvation has on cognitive function. Neurological logic is one of the first things to be sacrificed when a fragmented body is desperately clinging onto survival. Everything comes second to making sure that the heart keeps beating and the lungs keep breathing.

An Extract from Jane's Diary
November 2013

Hunger fogs my brain in the smoke of a world where the imaginary becomes reality and the things I thought were real are merely fabricated illusions. Absent of any capability of feeling real emotion, the place my mind and body has come to occupy is one where the numbness of my capacity to feel is echoed in the physical chill that leaves me constantly and unbearably cold. The landscape of my thoughts is absent of any of the colour and vitality which paints all true happy sentiment. Brushstrokes of sepia instead mimic the dredges of my wasted life.

With lack of energy comes an inability to concentrate and my attention span is non-existent. My attempts to string together logical thought processes merely result in tears formed out of frustrated exhaustion. Amidst my anxious fumbling around in this foggy headspace, finding a foothold - a focus – in the mundanity of everyday living has become an impossible ordeal. It is a bitter irony; the fact that my mind has become so preoccupied with an obsession with numbers that the number of things I am capable of contemplating, considering and addressing at one time, has been dramatically reduced.

This world does not seem to make sense anymore.

Many changes had been put into place by the time Jane got home from the hospital. Her bedroom had been moved into the dining room so that she did not over-exert herself going up and down the stairs and she now had a duvet to sleep on as well as a duvet to cover her. It was Mum's attempt to protect Jane's bones from breaking through her skin. The doormat had been replaced by her wheelchair and every time she wanted to cook or bake she had to sit at a stool rather than stand. Any action requiring "unnecessary" energy consumption was removed, for every scrap of energy consumed was needed to rebuild her body and could not be compromised.

Jane hated all of these changes. Whenever she could get away with "forgetting" to use her chair or sitting on her stool, she would. Most days she couldn't possibly use the downstairs toilet and so up the stairs she would climb. When no one was watching – which was very rarely – she would go into her empty bedroom and do crunches and sit-ups until she heard the floorboards on the landing squeak and she knew someone was nearby. Alex walked in on her on one occasion and she screamed at him to 'GET OUT'. Alex told Mum and when Mum confronted Jane she lied and told her Alex was making it all up. Mum yelled at Alex and told him he shouldn't lie. Alex cried and ran away. Rosie ran after him and, while she was gone, Jane told Mum that Alex was right – he hadn't been the one lying, she was. Again, love for her brother superseded, momentarily, the guilt of confessing her forbidden exercise. Jane felt a greater sense of guilt for allowing Mum to speak to Alex the way that she had.

Mum yelled at Jane, and deservedly so, but she couldn't run away like Alex, because Jane could not walk, never mind run.
Instead, she just stood there in silence.

Jane had applied to Oxford University to study English and, a week or so after her discharge, she had to go into Sixth Form in order to sit the aptitude test. She tried to keep her eyes focused on the floor as Dad wheeled her in, but she couldn't help looking up when she sensed a person close by. She was ashamed, but she also felt oddly powerful. She had achieved the goal she set a year ago - she was anorexic, even if anorexic meant a reality that was so very far from the attractive "skinny-ness" that she had craved. She didn't want anyone to see her in her chair, but at the same time she found herself thinking, would it be so bad if someone saw how thin she was now? She reckoned that maybe they would think she looked good. After all, she had been far too chubby the last time she was in college.

Jane's logic was skewed. It was no surprise that Oxford later emailed her a rejection. Still, she took it as a personal attack on the way she looked. The reason she had failed was obviously because she was too fat and too stupid, not because she had a mind so starved of nutrition that the essays she wrote made about as much sense as her dysmorphia.

Jane did not have a chance to return in person to the vegetarian restaurant that she had worked at since she was sixteen in order to say goodbye. It was her second home, a place that you couldn't leave without smelling like Spinach, Mushroom and Feta Curry or Puy Chilli Enchilada. It was a farewell which had to be done by text but she was reassured by her boss that the "sesame palace" would be waiting for her
as soon as you are ready, as soon as you are better.

* * *

The day Jane's boyfriend returned from the Politics trip that had begun during October half-term was the first day that all of these changes had to be explained to someone who wasn't her flesh and blood. Instead of listening to Postman Pat trundle along every morning with his black and white cat or, drinking nutritional supplements, Zak had spent the fortnight exploring Vietnam, blissfully unaware of the devastation unfolding back at home.

The day he returned was also the day he told Jane he loved her. It was Bonfire Night and she had been living at home for nearly a week.

Zak rang the doorbell and she answered, as she always had, with butterflies in her tummy and a nervous heart-skipping. A heart-skipping which made everything else seem utterly irrelevant. She could see his frame behind the glass of the door. She had missed him, that was a given, but for two weeks she hadn't had to worry about being touched. She wanted to show him how much she cared for him but she feared intimacy almost as much as she feared food. With a loss of weight came a loss of libido – and she assumed that her own repulsion at her body was shared by those most intimate with it – herself, her Mum and her boyfriend.

Mum could see that she was skin on bone. Jane could see rolls and rolls of fat. She thought Zak would see what she saw when, in reality, his and Mum's eyes were victim to the same skeletal silhouette. The mere notion of anyone seeing her body (or touching it) - whether it was a kiss or an arm around the waist - caused her extreme waves of anxiety. In his absence, she hadn't had to deal with this sensation for a while but, with his knock, it came rushing back, now ten times stronger.

Mum knew that the girl he was about to see wasn't the girl he had waved goodbye to a fortnight earlier - it was terrifying what had happened in such a short space of time. She was afraid to see how he would react. She knew he had a good heart, but he was a sensitive soul. Despite all the bravado and cheeky charisma that comes with being the class clown, Zak had a heart that was bigger than his rugby mates gave him credit for.

Mum waited with a strong cup of tea in the kitchen. Dad paced around the living room. Rosie and Alex hid in the bathroom upstairs – they just expected the usual hysterical outburst that occurred six times a day nowadays. They knew to keep their distance. Only Jane could explain what needed to be said and she had to do it alone, but she wasn't sure she knew what to say because she still couldn't quite understand it herself.

He stepped through the door and she was hit by his smell. She didn't have time to think before she was in his arms and he was telling her, for the very first time, he loved her.
She felt safe and warm and small - so very small.

They went into the dining-room-now-bedroom and sat on her bed. It was soft, he was soft and he smelled good. He was crying. She looked at him and she wiped his eyes and she said 'I'm anorexic.'

He nodded and said, 'I know.'

He told her that she would get better; that she would get through this.

After Zak had said his hello properly and given Jane the bear and Vietnamese paint set he had brought back with him, it was time for Jane to have her Fortisip. Every evening this would usually take Mum forty-five minutes. Constant consoling, incessant reassuring and now, more often than not, physically restraining her daughter in order to get her to drink her "medicine." On a particularly bad day, she had to get Dad to help her and the exertion and strain that their tiny missile of a child managed to exude actually caused Mum to have – what she thought – was a mini heart attack.

Jane would refuse.

Again and again and again,
screaming and yelling that it was 'too much',
that it would make her 'fat'
and that she hated herself.
She would start tugging at her arms
 and her face
 and her stomach
 and her thighs,
clenching her abdominal muscles and shaking her head with pursed lips as Mum desperately tried to put the straw in her mouth. Once the straw was there, in Jane's brain, there was nothing more she could do to fight it.

There were three criteria that had to be met:
1.   The dance of determined refusal must have gone on for forty-five minutes, minimum.
2.   She had to have physically fought as hard as she could to resist.
3.   The verbal and internal self-deprecation had to continue throughout the consumption as well as before and after.

If these were achieved then, in Jane's mind, she could tell the voice that she had tried and the guilt was momentarily lessened. Mum would stroke her hair as she supped, the sound of the sucking of the straw alternating with guttural sobs. After the deed was done, Jane would go into the toilet – not to make herself sick – but to commence a ritualistic punching of all the body parts she thought she could see getting fatter and fatter.

Her head for being weak,
her tummy for the ever-growing rolls of flab,

her arms for their thickness
and her thighs for their lack of thigh gap.

When Mum realised what Jane was doing, it wasn't because her daughter
told her.

One morning, she noticed some little blue marks peppering Jane's
forehead. They were clustered together in lines that matched the distance
between individual knuckles.
Tiny constellations formed out of the stars of shame.

When asked, Jane confessed almost instantly. Certain things she could
lie about as if they were second nature, but self-harm wasn't one of them.
Mum told her that every time she hurt herself, she would do the same. Jane
nodded, but she didn't think anything would come of it.

The next night she commenced the violent attack upon her body, but it
only lasted thirty seconds or so before she heard Mum screaming at her
to open the door. Usually, she would have ignored her, but her yells were
accompanied by a different sound this time – the soft thumping of Mum
punching herself too. This broke Jane's heart. She unlocked the door and
begged her to stop, the two of them red and flushed in violent exertion,
hot tears and cold pleas echoing through the hallway. She wrapped her
arms around Mum and, with four fists now preoccupied with an act of love,
rather than the impulse of hate, they stood as one, their heart rates slowing
to a steady lubdub. The next day when Jane woke up, a fresh midnight
blemish bloomed on Mum's forehead.

Jane's heart hurt.

Mum told the people at work that she had banged her head on a bookshelf
when they asked. It wouldn't do to confess her daughter's propensity for
self-harm.
Though the punching had come to a violent and distressing climax in
Mum's mirroring, Jane still felt "obliged" to go through the same torturous
process of hysterical refusal prior to every meal. Six times a day: breakfast,
mid-morning snack, lunch, mid-afternoon snack, dinner and finally, supper.
Today, however, she was too ashamed. She had company that wasn't her
family or a medical professional and the desire to keep up appearances
miraculously (and momentarily) superseded her need to fight her
prescribed dietary plan. She could not let Zak see how bad it had gotten.

So, she took her bottle and she returned to her seat on the bed. She held it in front of her and, all of a sudden, the cheery façade she had put up for the past hour since his arrival was replaced with a washed out, exhausted stare of fear.

Mum did not know what was going to happen.

She sat on Jane's left and Zak sat on her right and they exchanged a quick glance behind her back, their pity and dread almost as palpable as the fracas breaking out inside Jane's mind. The screams of anorexia to put up a fight you fat failure, just because he's here doesn't mean you drink it easily – fight it...FIGHT IT and the quiet whispers of rational Jane's encouragement - a Jane who wasn't poorly or tired or ashamed but a Jane who desperately wanted a return to normality – battled against each other in a deafening cacophony.

It was as if he knew, in that one look, what needed to be done.

The act of love that followed was the best thing he ever did for Jane. Zak stood up and he went into the kitchen. He took another bottle of Fortisip out of the fridge and shook it as he returned to the room. He sat back down, on her right, and he punctured the tinfoil top with the straw, then he took a good long suck and said 'that actually doesn't taste too bad.'

Mum was speechless.
Jane went into shock.
Zak sat there and he smiled.

He nodded at Jane and she looked back at the bottle in her own hands. She put the straw to her lips and she drank and, when it was over, he reached over and he held her hand and he laughed.

Mum wanted to squeeze Jane and tell her how proud she was but she was paralysed in the sheer awe of what had just happened. Though this was not to be a regular occurrence and Mum would have to deal with the fallout of Jane's guilt - a beast that would resurface with a vengeance mere hours later - she revelled in the moment, for it was the first time in months that she had allowed herself to feel the lightheaded electricity of hope.

They needed to act fast in order to make the most of this momentary return

to normality and Zak pulled Jane off the bed towards the hallway, holding tightly onto her hand. She was still frozen in the wake of what she had done and so she moved with automatic motion. They all piled into the back of the car; the Bonfire was only a few minutes away but, by the time they had arrived, she was starting to come around.
The regret was sickening.

She sat down in the wheelchair and Zak grasped the handles. This wasn't normal, none of it was. It could not have been easy for him - seeing his hockey-playing, cross-country-running, athlete of a girlfriend now crippled by an eating disorder and dependent on a wheelchair – yet he managed to keep his calm.

Jane did not have a chance to explode, the guilt was building, but there were people everywhere; family, friends and strangers. She could not make a scene. She would have to wait until Zak had left and she was safe to break down in the privacy of her home.

 It was a struggle, pushing Jane over the rough terrain of the field. Mum and Dad kept seeing colleagues and neighbours who were stunned at the sight of a girl they had known for near on a decade, suddenly being pushed around in a chair – a shadow of her former self.
A heart problem.
Oh, just an overactive thyroid.
Autoimmune disease.
They had their excuses ready, but anorexia was never one of them. It was too great a stigma. They knew what people said behind their backs and they did not want their daughter subjected to the stares and whispers that criticised her for making such a 'selfish' choice.

Toby was there with his girlfriend. He had been in Vietnam with Zak and this was also the first time he had seen Jane since the October half-term had begun. His face lit up in the light of the bonfire. He was not as good at hiding his feelings as his friend.

The fireworks started and Zak had got carried away in conversation. He didn't realise that Jane's chair was facing the opposite direction.

She was infuriated. She just wanted to get up and move it herself, but it took Toby's girlfriend to nudge Zak and point out that Jane was missing the show for him to realise his error and manoeuvre her so that she might see.

It was at this point that Zak could have turned around and said, 'No, Jane, I am so sorry but I can't do this'.

He did not.

He turned her chair around and he stood behind her and they watched the show together. After it was over, back they all bundled into the car and headed home. There was never a point where Zak gave up on Jane. There were many opportunities, but he never seemed to take them. He loved her and he wanted to be with her and, for a newly eighteen-year-old boy, it must have been terrifying. Yet, he stayed.

Sometimes it is the ones we least expect that turn out to be heroes. For a while, Zak was Jane's.

Chapter 5
Smile

Both Jane's parents were teachers.

Every morning, they would get up at 6am so that Mum could go through the breakfast sequence and still have time to make Jane's lunch, drive her to Grandma's and spoon-feed her her breakfast.

Yes, that is correct.
Spoon   feed.

Breakfast was one of the few meals where Jane was still able to eat "solid" food, rather than Fortisip, and Mum was desperate to keep it that way. After much discussion, argument and cursing of the dietician, they agreed that a Müller rice was the best thing for Jane to have. It was calorie dense so didn't fill her tummy too uncomfortably and, theoretically, shouldn't take too long to get Jane to eat. Unfortunately, of course, with the best will in the world, the dietician was wrong.

Jane had got to the point where she couldn't pick up her own spoon in order to put the rice pudding in her mouth – it was too much guilt for her to bear. This act fell to Mum.

The alarm would go off and Jane would wake up beside Mum.

After Jane had come back from the hospital, Mum had moved downstairs so that she could sleep next to her daughter. Jane needed the support both physically and mentally. Having Mum close made her feel safe and stopped her from exercising or doing anything during the night-time that would involve burning calories. Mum kept Jane warm and made sure that she was still breathing and, though her presence was not a necessity, she would never have forgiven herself if Jane had passed away in her sleep. This was a very real fear for her, now that her daughter was so small.

Just as new-borns sleep in their parents' room in a cot so that they can be monitored twenty-four seven, Mum and Dad had brought their own new-born home from the hospital. Jane needed an equal – if not greater – amount of supervision. The seventeen-year-old toddler was now rendered as fragile and vulnerable as a baby.

They would head into the kitchen after Jane had gone to the toilet and brushed her teeth.

Dad would already be in there, feeding the dog. As soon as they sat down at the table, Mum would nod to Dad that it was time for him to leave. The last thing Mum wanted to do was ostracise him in his own home, but Jane had to take priority – Jane was dying. She would whisper, 'I can't do it in front of him' – "it" being eating - and Mum would have to listen to her daughter – each spoonful of Müller rice was saving her life.

Jane could barely eat in front of Mum because the guilt was amplified when others were sat there watching her. She was paranoid and she felt judged. The more people around her, the greater the judgement – or "assumed" criticism she projected onto herself. By restricting Jane's audience to one, the pressure was somewhat alleviated and enabled her to focus on what was actually being said between her and her mother rather than what she thought other people were saying or thinking about her.

The whole process, from physically removing the lid of the carton to putting the spoon down at the end, was exhausting. The very first refusal occurred when Mum would tell Jane to eat the congealed grains of rice that had collected on the bottom of the lid. This was the protocol with all foil-lidded foods. After three weeks of trying – and failing - to persuade her to do this, eventually Mum had to give up. It wasn't worth it when the timeframe for getting Jane to eat the contents of the pot itself was so limited.

After about ten minutes, Mum would manage to get the spoon into Jane's mouth. No Momma-Bird "nee-naw- nee-naw open-wide!" playfulness. Just hysterics and begging. Once the spoon was there, there was nothing Jane could do except swallow. In the first few weeks, each mouthful would take between two and three minutes from spoon to stomach but, as Jane's guilt continued to get exponentially greater, the time for each spoonful also increased. The number of spoons she managed to get in reduced every day, despite Mum's valiant and unparalleled efforts. Jane was eating less, so her self-reproach should have also lessened, but, instead, she continued to fight the dwindling numbers with a voracious appetite for emptiness.

It was a mammoth battle and only the first of the day.

At 7:30am, the two of them would leave the house.

Mum and Dad both had full-time jobs, but Jane could not be left unsupervised for ten hours a day. Her situation was too severe. Mum and Dad had to find "day care" for their seventeen-year-old new-born, a role which fell to Grandma – Mum's Mum. Mum, Jane and the wheelchair would whizz down the road; Jane bundled up like a snowman in four or five layers of jumpers and coats and Mum, exhausted, red-eyed and flustered. She was no longer mentally prepared for the day ahead at work, how could she be, when she was terrified at what state her daughter would be in on her return home?

When they got to Grandma's house, before they got out of the car and headed inside, Mum would kiss her daughter on the forehead and tell her that she loved her. Every day, Jane would have with her a plastic bag containing a ham sandwich, a yoghurt and a Fortisip. Usually, Mum would be back from work to help her with the Fortisip, but, just in case she got held back, this was also Grandma's responsibility. Mum would say her goodbye to Jane in the car because, as soon as Mum came through the door, her focus automatically flipped to her dying father. She would make a beeline for his bedroom so that she could kiss his forehead, just as she had done Jane's, and hold his hand in hers to make it warm. Grandad was bed-bound and wholly dependent on his wife, just as Jane was on her mother.

Grandma and Grandad's house, number six, housed the poles of a human being's timeline. One man at the end of his days, a mind preoccupied with memories crafted carefully over a lifetime, no longer able to choose life over death. One girl – a toddler, a baby - with so much life ahead of her but blind to its promises, able to choose life over death's embrace but trapped in a mind-set that made seeing the beauty of this almost impossible.

Extract from Jane's Diary
November 2013

My soft skinned tawny owl with feathers of a whiskered chin and sapphires sparkling in deep set sockets, sits perched in a nest of pillows and papers which shuffle as he breathes and talks. Wise beyond your time, your big blue eyes smile at me and in that moment I know I'm the only thing you see and you're all I have room for in my heart.

I bundle in next to you and put my head against your chest. It's big and warm and I listen for the tick, tock, tick of the clock you told me they put inside your heart when I was five years old. I'm seventeen now, but I still press my face up tight to your ribs and listen to make sure you're still breathing and my guardian angel hasn't headed back up to those bright heavenly heights just yet. You're my grandfather clock, a living breathing mahogany cabinet, but you aren't full of the echoes and reverberations of a brass pendulum. No. Yours is a case which holds the secrets of a lifetime, the whispers of a war and international adventures found only in the realms of a dream, swinging in jazzy rhythms to the soundtrack of your history, back and forth, back and forth... Sinatra and Nat King Cole waltzing on strips of magnetic black magic that run in loops inside clear plastic cassettes.

When I am sat beside you, the voices aren't so loud. I wish I could nestle here forever because I feel small and safe and loved. I do not believe I am worthy of anyone's love, especially not my own, but yours is inescapable and so I cannot help but let myself feel it. You and Mum are the same. She loves you more than you could possibly imagine. I hate that I'm taking her away from you.

I wish she could sit here, with you and I, and the three of us could rest and be peaceful in this cloud of warmth together. Unfortunately though, life doesn't work like that. It never does really.

After Mum left, Jane would talk to Grandma in the kitchen for a while and then head up to the attic to "study" before her morning snack. This comprised of 400ml of milk which Grandma would measure out into a cup under Jane's scrutinous observation. She would then leave the cup on the windowsill before she jumped in the shower, every day like clockwork at 9am. As soon as the bathroom door closed, Jane would come down from the attic and pour half of the milk down the sink. She would then refill the cup up to the 400ml line with cold water so that Grandma was clueless to the substitution.

Job one – Done.

Next, she would go to the fridge where the ham sandwich was wrapped in tinfoil. She would undo it – as gently and silently as she could – and pull out as much of the ham as would be unnoticeable. Sometimes Grandma would forget her head towel and open the bathroom door before the usual time of 9:07am. Petrified, Jane would jam the door of the fridge shut, her heart in her mouth and temples sweating with the fear of being caught. Grandma's house was her only opportunity to be deceitful and she could not risk that being taken away.

She would use the ham she had taken from the sandwich to wipe as much butter as was feasibly possible from the bread. Then, she would put the buttery slice of pork in a napkin, crumple it up and hide it underneath the other rubbish in the bin. As she got more and more savvy with removing the filling, she began cutting off millimetres of the crusts of the sandwich triangles, pushing each down flat with her palm so that it looked as if it was the same size as before she had trimmed it. Into the paper towel the crusts would go, joining their fellow fallen comrades in the graveyard of deceit at the bottom of the kitchen bin.

Job two – Done.

Job three involved the physical fight which, though significantly less violent than the one she put up against her mother, had to occur before she could allow Grandma's arthritic fingers to pry open her lips and place the little pieces of sandwich gently inside her mouth.
'Good girl, that's it now. Come on, swallow.'

An eighty-year-old lady feeding a bird and a stubborn one at that.

Grandma was good at the talking part, mainly because she administered tough love. She would tell Jane about how, as a girl, she had been terrified of swallowing because when she was an infant she had nearly choked on a shoe buckle.

'Come on Jane, that's it.'
Jane shook her head. Her lips pursed.
'Now you stop being so silly young lady! What's all this, hmm?'
Grandma pushed the tiny square of bread between Jane's lips.
Jane shook her head so vigorously that Grandma dropped the sandwich.

'Excuse me, Jane! Stop it! Right now!'
Jane burst into hysterics. Her lips remained tightly closed. She wanted to

apologise to Grandma. She wanted to yell: I can't, I won't, don't make me!
But as soon as she opened her mouth, she knew that Grandma's sharp,
arthritic fingertips would swoop in. Like a mother feeding a baby. Grandma
had been a nursery assistant in her youth; she was used to uncooperative
infants.

'If you don't open your mouth right now, I'm calling your mother! And
then she'll have to come home from work and how the Hell is she going to
explain that, eh? Do you want to be responsible for that, Mrs.?' Jane shook
her head, her tears now soft but constant. 'Right, I thought not.'

Grandma paused whilst she picked up another square of sandwich.
'Now then' – a gentler tone, 'I know this is hard poppet, I know, but, if I
can get over swallowing, you can eat this tiny piece of bread, ok?'

Grandma turned to the sink and pulled a piece of kitchen roll off of the side.
She folded it gently and wiped the wetness off Jane's cheeks.
'Ok, Jane.' Jane opened her lips a millimetre or so, 'That's it, sweetheart',
Grandma pushed the bread through the tiny gap, 'Good girl', Jane's lips
closed.

'Now swallow, swallow, sw-aah-loo-ow!'
Jane looked at her. Terrified. The sandwich sat on her tongue, saliva
pooling around it. Grandma was old and beautiful and full of fire. Jane
couldn't swallow. She wanted to. She couldn't. She had to.

'If you don't swallow in the next three seconds, I'm calling your mother.'
Jane did not doubt it.
'One'
She couldn't. She wouldn't. She challenged Grandma with her eyes.
Grandma matched her gaze. Neither blinked.

'Two'
No, no, no, no! Jane shook her head, the sandwich shaking around inside
her mouth like a maraca.

'Three!'
She swallowed.
Guilt at what she was making the eighty-year-old do broke the wall. The
wall between spit and swallow. The wall between life and death.
After the "meals", Jane would go and sit with Grandad. It was the only time

she would not feel guilty for voluntarily being at rest.

Grandad Peter could see she was upset. He could hear the chaos occurring in the kitchen, but he never said a word. He held her hand and he squeezed it tightly in his and he looked deep into her eyes and he sang to her. 'Smile, though your heart is aching. Smile, even though it's breaking. When there are clouds in the sky you'll get by. If you smile through your fear and sorrow. Smile and maybe tomorrow, you'll see the sun come shining through for you.' She would smile and the tears that fell down her cheeks were formed out of the purest kind of love.

Jane was still a human being. She still had the capacity to care even if, to the outsider, it looked as if she was being utterly selfish. The guilt for the way she was destroying her family was even greater than the guilt she had for eating. It is why she still ate, why she never actually went a day without consuming some form of nutrition. She could not bear the agony and the sadness that she was raining down on those who loved her the most. Grandad was slowly dying of heart failure and, if Jane kept on going the way she was, it could well be a joint funeral.

When she wasn't sitting with Grandad, making him and Grandma lunch or, being finger-fed ham sandwiches, Jane was upstairs in the attic studying for her exams. This involved opening the window as wide as she could, removing all of her clothes and jogging on the spot as silently as possible. Grandma never went upstairs and Grandad was bed-bound, so there was never any risk of them catching her out.

For Jane, this was one of her lowest points. Naked, shivering and jogging on the spot so that she could burn off the calories that were the only thing stopping her from collapsing into a heap of bones and twisted thoughts.

For five weeks and six days, this was Jane's routine.

Jane was being weighed on Mondays and Fridays at the outpatient clinic. Usually, Mum would take her, but sometimes Dad would go as well. On those days, Jane sat in the back of the car in stony silence and refused to engage with her parents at all. She knew that, whatever the outcome – gain or loss - Dad's reaction would infuriate her because he couldn't hide his emotions as well as Mum. If Mum was relieved at Jane gaining a little weight, she knew not to show it or mention it, because this would make her daughter feel even worse. If Dad was there, he would congratulate her

– even though Mum had warned him not to do so – because he couldn't help himself. His face would light up if it was a gain and drop if it was a loss and both of these expressions made Jane feel sick to her stomach. It wasn't Dad's fault but Jane always managed to find a way to make it such. She projected her own self-hatred onto him and, no matter what he did to try and deflect it, he couldn't – Jane was an expert.

A Letter from Jane to Megan - Extracts

I soon went from weekly observations to bi-weekly and Jemma would bleed those veins of mine dry. I used to hate having my blood taken, mainly because it was so excruciatingly painful. My arms were literally skin on bone and so, breaking that skin, even the mere pinprick of a needle, was rather uncomfortable to say the least. As the weeks went on and the threat of admission loomed closer, I knew I needed to do something to convince them I was actively trying to get better and this is where I learnt how to "layer up" and "water load".

Water load: Water weighs. The rest is pretty obvious.

Lots of layers are easy to explain when you are underweight. You are perpetually freezing. Granted, three pairs of tights are probably a little too extreme BUT every gram counts when your weight is the single thing keeping you at home and out of inpatient services. I never had an issue with being too warm and so I would wear as many clothes as I could get away with in order to get the professionals off my back. However, they soon cottoned on and I had to find new ways to disguise the rapid weight loss which preoccupied my every thought and action.

This is where water loading came into play.
In the first instance, this was pretty easy. A pint of water just before we drove to outpatients and I would be in the clear for another few days but, as I lost more weight, I needed to drink a lot more and there is obviously a limit to one's bladder capacity. I developed a rather impressive ability to control the desire to wee; keep distracted. But it got to the point where, as soon as I had been weighed, I would need to go to the toilet and, despite desperately attempting to hide this, Jemma soon demanded that Mum go to the toilet with me.

Dr E gave me an ultimatum; gain a kilo in a week. If not, it was option one or option two, both of which I really, really did not want to have to contemplate but, as the numbers stagnated and slowly began to drop (no matter how much I drank), I was forced to face reality.

1. I could voluntarily take the empty bed at the inpatient unit, but this was not something I had any desire to do willingly.
2. They would section me and sections are not something which will disappear from your medical record as swiftly as an STI.

Friday the 13th, 2013, was the day that Jane's battle became shared. The day that the responsibility for her recovery was removed from solely herself and given to an inpatient support team.

The weeks that led up to that point were utter hell.

They were a period that saw breakdown after breakdown – not just for Jane and Mum and Dad, but also for Rosie and Alex. On one occasion, Mum and Dad had to stay late after work and Rosie – fifteen-year-old Rosie – was responsible for watching her sister.

Jane had had her "supper" and ran up to the bathroom. For the next thirty minutes she brushed her teeth in a fit of hysterics, the desperately aggressive strokes making her gums bleed as she tried to get the taste of yoghurt off her tongue. Rosie sat opposite her while she manically spat minty white bubbles into the toilet basin. As time went on, the white went brown as blood filled her mouth. Most of the foam was coating her face and t-shirt in a mixture of snot and tears and chalky gunk and, in between holding her sister's hand and wiping her eyes with a towel, Rosie spoke softly to her with soothing, non-judgmental empathy. When it was over and Jane was too exhausted to stand, Rosie pulled her up, guided her into her room, changed her T-shirt and told her it was all going to be OK. They sat on the carpet and she calmed her till Mum got home. Two weary sisters, forehead to forehead, the younger now so much older in everything but age.

When they were small, Granny Sally used to sing to them a song called 'Sisters' that she had sung with her sisters when she was a girl too, 'Sisters, sisters, there were never such devoted sisters. Never had to have a chaperon, no sir, I'm here to keep my eye on her. Caring, sharing, every little thing that we are wearing.'
Rosie became Jane's best friend as soon as she set eyes on her.
She was 'Snow White' and Rosie was 'Rose Red'. For fifteen years Jane set

an example, made all of the mistakes first and gave Rosie all of the advice she wished she had had when she was Rosie's age. They performed in ballet recitals together, ran around the garden jumping in and out of the paddling pool and had matching purple velour dresses for the nativity at church on Christmas Eve, but then, just like that, the dynamic changed, and Rosie had to become the big sister for a while - the strong one.

When Jane was in the hospital after one particularly bad episode, Rosie said the most honest thing anyone had said to her since the whole nightmare began. She told her that it 'wasn't fair'.

Not because she was being mean to Dad or taking Mum away from her and Alex. She knew that that wasn't something Jane had chosen. What was unfair, was that she didn't have a sister anymore. She had had one, for fifteen years and then, one day, she was gone. Anorexia had stolen her away and she needed her back. Rosie was born second. She wasn't meant to be suffering all of the struggles of her teenage years alone - it was why Jane was born first. Jane had a purpose and that purpose was Rosie and Alex – her siblings needed her just as she needed them but, rather than support them, she had exposed them to the brutal reality of living with an eating disorder.

Alex was only thirteen when his sister stopped eating.

He was so traumatised by her illness that he thought he had "caught" it himself. One morning, he woke up and he wasn't hungry. He didn't understand why. He didn't understand what anorexia was. Mum and Dad kept telling him that Jane was poorly but he couldn't comprehend why she was poorly, because they didn't know how to explain it.

Mental illness is a tumour-less cancer.

They could tell him a thousand times that his sister was mentally ill, that she had an eating disorder, that she was anorexic, but they didn't know why.

'Why' was Alex's eternal question;
'Why is she doing this?'
'Why is she poorly?'
'Why is she being so mean to Dad?'
'Why is she covered in bruises?'

'Why is she doing sit-ups in her room with the door closed?'
'Why is she in hospital?'
'Why doesn't she come to school with us anymore?'
'Why is she so skinny?'
'Why does she make so much food but never eat it?'
Why, why, why.

Sometimes the 'why's' would be interspersed with other questions, questions Mum still didn't know the answer to, but ones she had to try and find a way of answering with a hope that she herself now struggled to find.

'Is she going to die?'	No.
'Will she get better?'	Of course.
'When?'	I don't know Al, I'm sorry.
'Is it contagious?'	No son, don't worry, you won't catch it.
'Why is she starving herself?'	Because she has an eating disorder, it's called **anorexia.**

One day, Mum found Alex crying in the kitchen. In front of him was half of a baguette. She asked him what was wrong and he told her he wasn't hungry, but he was forcing himself to eat it because he was terrified he had caught Jane's disease.

She took it away and she sat down beside him and she told him to look her in the eye.

'Alex, trust me. You cannot catch anorexia. If you aren't feeling hungry, you don't have to eat! Everyone has their off days. Listen to your body and give it what it needs when it needs it. You are fine. Jane has a mental illness, which means she doesn't see herself the way we see her. Part of her anorexia is a condition called 'body dysmorphia', which means she doesn't see what we see. It isn't as if she can see how small she is and keeps starving herself nevertheless. She literally looks in the mirror and all she sees is fat.

You can't catch it, Alex. Please trust me. You are going to be fine, OK?'

After that conversation, Alex had some of his questions answered. They still remained in his mind, but he had a better grasp of why and that was all that Mum could give him. It helped him get through the heartbreak that coloured every day a dismal grey and, though it wasn't much, it was something. They were days of pain and fear and desperation for it was a time absent of hope and permeated with panic, but ultimately, the five of them, Jane's family, pulled through.

To get through what they did during that time was a miracle, but it was possible.

It is possible.
The reason why? Love.

Chapter 6
Friday the 13th

An Extract from Jane's Diary
November 2013
Every morning I wake with the same gnawing hunger in my stomach.

Every morning I go through the same process.
First the thighs, a squeeze and sigh as the skin thickens between my fingertips. What is merely loose flesh, I assume to be fat. Flab.
Next, the hip bones. Jagged summits that rise out of my pelvis and catch on every window ledge, every table leg, every countertop. They are purple, like my arms, attracting sharp corners like magnets. The blooms which colour my hip bones are darker in colour and ever so slightly green around the edges. These ones hurt more, but I guess part of me takes pride in the fact that the bones are so pronounced now that, with just a little more pressure next time I bump, they might break through my skin completely.
My fingers are cold. Always cold. They trace the line of my ribcage (pretty prominent for weeks now) along my sternum and up to my collar bone. Here, they rest for a while. Smoothly stroking the bone from left to right, all the way across to where the nodules of my shoulder joints make craters in my skin. Milk silk soft.
I am content. Momentarily.
But then my fingers dance up to my face and, in the darkness of my room, they pull and stretch and squeeze the soft mass of my cheeks. What initially resembled shiny globes of health, dimpled Gala apples, is now a taught pale sheet of white, starched with dried tears and the soft brush of Laguna hair – my body's reaction to the perpetual cold I inhabit.
And that is that.

With the slow stream of hot tears catching in the tips of my eyelashes, comes the morning. The morning and a fresh hell on the horizon.

My routine is the only piece of normality I have left.

Nothing is normal anymore for I am not normal. The hatred I feel for my body is omnipresent. It never stops. Every window, every mirror, every time I pick up my phone and see my reflection, ugly in the glass. Do other people feel this way? Do other people think this way? Oh, to have a silent mind. To eat without fear of the inevitable outcome. The consequences I have taught myself to take as gospel. My own religion. Founded on worship absent of love. This is a cult obsessed with self-destruction. A bible written by me for me and only me. I, who stand solitary as the victim of its criticism.
I pray for release, but release never comes.

Every day I face the same challenges and I do not know if I can do this anymore.

There is no cure. I see no cure. They speak of a moment, a lightbulb flash when everything suddenly makes sense and I can find what normal people call normal again, but I do not believe them. I do not have hope for I have not the energy to be hopeful. I am tired and cold and everything aches, but still she screams at me that I am fat and that is that.
There is never a moment where all of me is acceptable, there is always something wrong. Something too chunky. Something too chubby. Some fold of flab or glaring spot. Sideways, profile, portrait, full length, half body, face, feet, fingers FAT. Always fat. My constant thought. Fat.

When I feel my way across my body every morning, before the sunlight breaks through the curtains, I think about how other girls my age start theirs. Perhaps they wake up and fall straight back to sleep again – 6am is too early to be dragging themselves up and out to the breakfast table. Perhaps their fingers do not spend time mapping the mountains that rise out of their pelvis and playing the xylophone of their ribcage. Maybe, instead, their curious hands find other ways to explore their bodies, the sexual awakening of their late teens encouraging curious minds to ascertain what it is that brings them the greatest pleasure. I wonder what fills their heads. Dreams of university, dreams of love, dreams of a weekend spent drinking and dancing and deferring all real-life responsibilities to later. Later Mum, I'll do it later.
I wish I could do this later. Actually, no, I wish I did not have to do any of this at all.

I wish I could wake up and rest my hands peacefully on my chest, feeling my heartbeat slow as I remember it was all a dream and that, actually, I am normal. I wish I was waking up in my bedroom, not the dining-room-now-bedroom, and that the window was open, letting in the morning. Clean and cold.

I wish I was dreading going into school for a mock examination, knowing I had fallen asleep going over my notes the night before and hadn't reached Mao's Foreign Policy. I wish I then remembered that Zak and I had made plans for after college that day, a drive to the beach and some frozen pineapple, paling any fear for my mock into insignificance and making my gentle heartbeat soar into spectacular rhythm.
It has been a while since it peaked 40BPM.
I wish I did not dread breakfast. Toast and butter to get me through the morning's classes. I wish I suddenly sat bolt upright as I realised that I had forgotten. That actually, I had no class this morning, because I was captaining my hockey team at an away game at Barnard Castle.

All these wishes, all these dreams echo through my broken body.
I feel the grin of a victory on the pitch twitch at the corners of my mouth and I taste the sweet tang of residual pineapple on Zak's lips as he nuzzles my face with his stubble. I sense the bubbling of nerves as I sit in the loft of the history block, a white sheet of paper turned upside down on the desk in front of me.

These are not big dreams to be rich and famous and remembered for doing something rather remarkable. They are not ridiculously absurd wishes, like owning a private jet or being Prom Queen. They are just the desires of an ordinary seventeen-year-old girl to do ordinary things. To be normal. To think normal things and fear normal fears.

And then I remember.
I remember that I am not normal and none of this is normal and I roll to my side and I feel Mum's soft breath on my face as she murmurs that it is time to get up.

The Hell of breakfast is impending, I just wish I could continue dreaming.

On the morning of Friday the 13th, Jane had consumed (as would later come to light) the equivalent of a kilo of liquid.

As the weeks had gone by, she had been losing weight – slowly but surely – and, though she had managed to disguise it well with water loading and additional layers of clothing, as the weight dropped she needed to consume more and more water in order to disguise it. It meant that, though the volume of water she was drinking prior to her appointments was getting ever greater, her weight appeared to be "maintaining" itself and, with this, the promise of an inpatient admission had become more serious.

This particular Friday, Jane had been given an ultimatum: gain the required 500g or the bed that had become available in the inpatient unit at the beginning of the week would be hers. These beds were rare and Jane's psychiatrist made it very clear to Mum and Dad at their monthly assessment meeting that, if one came up, Jane should take it. There was no doubt about it. If Jane refused and her weight continued to fall the way it had been, they would have no choice but to threaten her with being sectioned.

Mum and Dad wanted nothing more than to help their daughter to recover at home, but they knew that Jane was in need of serious help; she wasn't the same person they had known for the last seventeen years. It was beyond frightening. Her behaviours had been absurd when they had brought her home from the paediatric wing, but now they were bordering on crazy. Jane was aware of the severity of the situation. Friday the 13th was judgement day, her freedom depended on it. There was no way that she could mess it up.

An Extract from Jane's Diary
December 2013

The water had been putting pressure on my bladder for at least two hours. I was desperate for the toilet, but I knew that, today of all days, I needed to exercise extreme self-control and, I did.

Stepping on the scales and closing my eyes, I tried to focus on anything but the convulsing agony throbbing in my abdomen. Jemma scribbled something down on her notepad and I took that as a good sign. She murmured something to Mum and I asked, 'did I do it?'
Her hesitant nod told me all I needed to know and I grinned.
No more empty inpatient threats but, more importantly, now I could finally pee. I put my coat back on. I knew I needed to get out of the consultation room quickly. But Mum didn't move.

She clearly didn't believe that I had gained. She turned to Jemma and said, 'would you mind weighing her again? We are going to go to the toilet.' Jemma told her that this was what she was about to suggest anyway. The pain in my bladder evaporated. It was replaced with the plummeting of my stomach to my toes, so quickly, that I thought I was going to throw up. 'I don't need the toilet' I lied, through a semi-hysterical whisper.

'You're going' said Mum. There was nothing I could do to stop her.

Half dragging, half leading, Mum took my hand and led me to the toilet. She sat in the cubicle next to me.
"Ok, just a little bit" I thought. I can control how much I urinate. I am in control. But, as I sat there, three pairs of tights loosely wrapped around my ankles, sweating for the first time in months from sheer terror, I lost it. Lost control completely.
 As the sting of excess fluid pressing on my insides was relieved, it was replaced with an even deeper pain. A pain that gutted me and knocked my breath from my chest. It was pain that wasn't quite pain, more like dread. Painful dread.

The sheer, unparalleled fear of what I had done.

As Jane walked back to the medical room, she knew. So did Mum.

She reached out and grasped Mum's hand, for there was nothing that needed to be said. She was exhausted from the sheer emotional and physical exertion that anorexia had subjected her to over the past fifteen months. An admission meant that anorexia had lost the battle, professionals were now intensely involved. People that weren't Jane's people. People that weren't her family and Zak. Those people, professional people, were now invested in her recovery, but Jane was far from victorious just yet. Fixing the body is so very far from fixing the mind. If it were that easy, eating disorders would not exist.

Four doctors, two psychiatrists and three stone gone, Jane sat in the waiting room, a shell of a person, not a woman but a girl. Around her, nurses whizzed about, making the necessary phone calls and confirming her bed at the unit. Mum was outside on the phone to Dad. As she told him the news, there was relief in her broken voice. Though she felt like they had failed her, that they were responsible for their little girl's cursed metamorphosis, she knew that the admission to Ward 13 was a good thing. It meant that Jane would not be able to cater to the demands of her demons as she had at home. Despite their efforts to protect her - she would have the professional support she needed to fight them, and this was all that they could ask.

Mum had to have hope, she had to be strong for her little girl because her little girl needed all the strength that she could get.

In the moments before Mum came back inside, Jane experienced a moment of peace.

The voice, the cancer of anorexia, which had pulled the Jane down from the heights of a wondrous childhood, finally stopped.
Just for a second.

The screaming and the yelling and the berating of the last year just stopped and the silence was deafening.

It was as if the illness, the dark part of Jane's psyche that had, for so long, smothered her light, realised it was now under attack, for it wasn't up to Jane anymore. Ward 13 meant a total loss of agency. The responsibility for her physical recovery was now taken from Jane's hands. Finally, she had no option left but to fight back. It was inescapable and, in anorexia's shock, Jane experienced the euphoria of silence.

The bliss of nothing.

An Extract from Jane's Diary
December 2013

In that beautiful puddle of quiet I regained, momentarily, the clarity of thought which I had lost so long ago, A moment of calm that saw logic and reasoning finally resurface. I knew that this was not going to be easy. It was not going to be a click of the fingers and a miraculous one-hundred-and-eighty-degree flip in perspective. No, it would take time, so much time. I knew that I could not focus on anything else for the foreseeable future because there would not be a future if I didn't stop the spiral. I was going to die if I didn't get my shit together. I didn't want to die. I couldn't, because it wouldn't just be the end of my life, it would be the end of my family's too.

By the time Mum returned, Jane was utterly drained. The second round of tears came in the car on the way home. They pulled up and Dad was waiting on the driveway. He hugged them both, his two red-eyed girls, and Jane let him because she didn't know how long it would be before he could hug her again. He went over to the boot of his car and pulled out a photo frame. Jane took it, tentatively, from his hands and, as soon as she saw what was inside it, the third wave of sobbing commenced. It was a collage of around fifty thumb-sized photos of Jane and her friends that they had put together. They didn't know that Jane was going into an inpatient unit, but she hadn't been at school for a month and they wanted to give her something to remind her of how loved she was.

They packed her bag and drove back to the inpatient unit, Ward 13, where the three of them met with Jane's outpatient psychiatrist in the family room. Jane could see the other children. There were eleven of them. They stared at her as she came in through the automatic doors and nudged each other, whispering as they assessed how sick this new addition to their ward was. No matter how experienced the staff, how high-tech the monitoring systems or how well-practised the policies, eating disorders are inherently competitive. Anorexia does not take into account someone else's muscle mass, height or weight. In an eating disorder unit, competition and comparison are just as prevalent as panic attacks.

> All an eating disorder sees is someone skinnier.
> Someone more strong-willed.
> Someone figuring out a way to lose weight despite constant supervision.

Jane was in a place that they hoped would save her life, but she was now living with eleven individuals just as sick, if not sicker. Her battle with food was joined by the ally of incessant comparison. A partnership of the most lethal kind.

After the psychiatrist had told them the ins and outs of the generic daily routine, they took Jane to her room. The nurse told her that she was in luck because it was the best one in the unit. As soon as she stepped through the door, the first thing Jane saw was the private bathroom. She thought that this was good. It meant that, if she played her cards right, she could still find a way to exercise. Her thinking patterns were still rooted in deceitful impulse.

On her bedframe was an air mattress, specifically designed to relieve the pressure on her bones. It moved up and down automatically and made sounds that mimicked her own breathing whilst the motion matched the rise and fall of her chest. It would eventually be one of the only things that could help soothe her when she was restless and unable to sleep prior to being weighed on Monday and Thursday mornings.

Mum helped her unpack and Dad stood outside in the hallway. The photo frame the girls had made her sat proudly on her desk – memories of a happier time when food was not the enemy and she had the freedom of movement to dance and drink and be an extraordinarily ordinary teenage girl. There were photos from parties they had gone to the summer before, pictures of them on Duke of Edinburgh expeditions and at their Fifth Year Prom. Every picture was a portrait of a smiling stranger; a girl with the same big brown eyes and thick black hair. The only difference was her face. It wasn't gaunt and lined with fatigue or pained with the constant fear of being fat. It was rosy, blushed with innocence and vitality, for the mind that lay behind it was free of self-deprecation, self-hatred and self-disgust. Jane and Mum stood in front of the frame and, when Mum looked to her right she saw silent tears rushing down her daughter's cheek. She had seen Jane cry - far too many more times than a mother should have to witness in the last few months - but these
were a different type of tears. They were nostalgic and they were gentle in their sadness. They weren't visceral and violent tirades of hysterical anger and hatred – they were reminiscent of better days. Brighter ones.

Twenty or so minutes later, the nurse came in and told them that it was time for Jane to have her dinner. Mum squeezed Jane's hand and told her to be brave. She said that they would be back before supper with Rosie and Alex and that she was just on the other end of the phone if Jane needed her.

This was the first time that Mum hadn't sat beside her daughter and fed her her evening Fortisip for six weeks. Jane was beyond petrified.

Mum wheeled her up the corridor and, when they got to the front door, the nurse took the handles from her.

Mum waved goodbye to her seventeen-year-old toddler as she embarked upon her first day at the nursery school of inpatient care. The same sense of loss gutted her as had done when she said farewell at the gate to St George's Nursery School, twelve years ago. She had to muster every ounce of strength she had left in order to try and keep her composure. Jane's life was about to start again but, as she trundled in her chair towards the dining room for the very first time, it wasn't the excitement of making new friends and playing in the sandpit that preoccupied her. Instead, it was the thrum of her heartbeat and its anxious flutter. It was her realisation that she was now rendered completely vulnerable in her independence – eating must be by her own hand and her own hand alone.

Letting go of Mum's was the first step but, unlike in nursery school, at the end of the day, she wasn't going home. They couldn't sit in the kitchen and bake banana bread whilst watching the Teletubbies or play rubadubdub with plastic floats in the sink. This was a long school day - nearly four months long to be precise. Jane would not be the same person that sprinted out into Mum's arms after the final bell rang.

The Jane that would emerge would be a warrior, her riptide now finally under control.

Chapter 7
Ward 13

An Extract from Jane's Diary
March 2017

Sometimes I find myself thinking about them, my fellow nightingales. Especially now my body is starting to slip into that same silhouette again and the thoughts are screaming louder. I miss them, my nurses too - the ones who never stopped trying.

For nearly four months, they became my family and, to them, I owe my life. Though three years have passed and I haven't seen any of them since the day I left, I can remember each and every one of their faces, just like it was yesterday. One of them is about to go to university to become a doctor. One of them has a baby them on the way. One of them wrote back to me a year or so after I was discharged and one of them left England and travelled the world. One of them still isn't quite out of the woods just yet and one of them is still fighting her, every single day. One of them became a mental health nurse and a couple of them went to college. Each and every one of them is a survivor and, for that, I could not be prouder, not only to have known them, but also to have loved them.

We chose life, albeit in our own time.

It makes me smile to think about the time we spent together, mainly because the majority of the memories I have are not steeped in sadness. They aren't saturated in shock at the desperate and ridiculous lows we would stoop to in order to lose weight. They aren't even laced with regret. In all honesty, it is more the comedy of our actions I remember and I think it is because I am at peace with leaving the darker stuff where it happened – remembering those parts isn't worth the trauma.

My fellow patients provided me with a little bit of light in what was an incredibly dark part of my life. I do not think I ever thanked them enough. I should have. I should have thanked them for the cards with kind words of encouragement, for the smiles of an unparalleled empathy. For the hugs when we waited in line for the examination room on weigh-days and for the conspiracy theories that got us through post-meal PTSD. From the knitting and the nail painting to the occupational therapy letter-writing and 'Justdance' competitions when we were deemed "healthy" enough. We pulled each other through those days and I think I only really appreciate it now that I face this battle alone. Again...

The time I spent in Ward 13 was far from easy, but they made it memorable. Memorable in the right way. They were the only people who ever truly knew how hard my struggle was because they were experiencing it themselves. However hard they tried, the experience of an eating disorder was never something that our doctors and nurses could ever truly relate to. They were blessed with a mind free of anorexia's ventriloquism. In their peace, they could not understand why we thought the way we did, why we acted with such a lack of fear for consequence. It was absurd to them that, when we were left momentarily alone, we would lock ourselves in our bathrooms and do crunches until they knocked on our bedroom doors and called us for dinner.

Each and every one of them, deserves the world. I hope that life brought them peace or that, at least, they are getting there. I hope that they haven't found a friend in her again. All anorexia does is bring pain.

Living in Ward 13 wasn't simple.

An Extract from Jane's Diary
December 2013

Hands begin their daily dance.

Anxiety speaks to unconscious tapping as finger to thumb they commence their routine.

Tentative.
I lower my feet onto the polished plastic floor.
Twitching Digits
Maniacal in their increasing tempo

Flicker in pulses of paranoia as the drum of mental
           Asphyxiation
Strikes a beat.

I see children
(They are children)

Trudging through the vanguard of their own minds
Sheltering from air raids of doubt which shower shrapnel of self-
deprecation in splinters of plates and cups and cutlery upon them
Facing an enemy with the same tired eyes
In every mirror
Every window
Each unforgiving sheet of glass.

They droop in lines of withered daffodils
Turning away from a sun called HOPE and weeping seeds of a forlorn
fatigue onto
Arms marked with the road map of desperation
Attempts to achieve absolution.

There is no armistice
No ceasefire
No hope for the hand of friendship.

Instead these
Echoes of happier times

Are hopeless.

We are all the same.
Frantically scanning with sunken eyes and bony fingers
Our shivering frames
Perched.
Starving canaries   trapped
In cages of perpetual apprehension.

The only way out
to partake in a universal necessity.
An act we have come to associate with Guilt
Weakness

Gluttony
Fat.

Yet every day
Six times a day
We sit.

Hunger pangs yawning in our guts masking self-consumption as self-control.

Empty wheelchairs waiting
We emerge from silver spun cocoons
Threads of silk as delicate and breakable as our bones.
Nightingale now warrior
Praying for our new found wings to lift us into something better
Somewhere safer.

Into the battleground of our minds we venture and afore us stand
Our demons – Ourselves
'Twenty minutes'
She calls.

Exhausted
Hot tears slide down cold dead flesh
Curtains of this terror made manifest
Sweeping in shadows across the painfully emaciated canvas of her face.

The clock starts. Through salty tears she stares.

It was, however, enlightening.

In the early days of Jane's admission, she kept herself to herself.

She didn't want to be there; she didn't want to recover. Her dependence on Fortisip soon extended to every single one of the six meals prescribed to her on a daily basis and this was partly due to the habits her fellow patients possessed. Competition was everywhere. If the others drank Fortisip, she would too. Fortisip was more common at the dinner table than solid food and the constant residual stench of the after-taste that caught on the patients' breath permeated the corridors and communal areas.

The smell was worsened in the patients who had had to resort to the nasogastric tube. They carried the little bag of Fortisip around with them. Some of the bank staff nurses would knit sleeves to cover the bag with patterns of turtles or multicoloured stripes. They hoped it would lessen the shame that the patients felt, but nothing could disguise the yellowing cord that ran along their chest and up into their nose.

 Little porcelain dolls being pumped with beige blood.

Though Jane knew that she could never deign to that level of dependence – it would make her recovery even more impossible than it already seemed – it triggered her into refusing to consume any form of solid food, not even the yoghurts or Müller rices which she had, at least, managed at home.

On arrival to the Ward, the hardest battle Jane faced was physically putting the straw in her own mouth. Mum had done this for her for the last six weeks and the guilt she experienced the first time she managed to bring it to her lips of her own accord had catastrophic consequences.

It crippled her. The hysterical and self-deprecating outburst which followed rendered her too much of a risk, too much of a trigger, to the other patients to allow her to sit with them in the living room during the compulsory thirty-minute post-meal observation. She was taken to a smaller therapy room where two nurses sat and tried to talk her down. It took them hours.

Post-meal observations were essential in order to prevent the patients from vomiting or exercising, but Jane's issue was neither. She had regressed into her old ways - violent outbursts of self-harm. With Mum no longer present, the punching recommenced – though long after mealtimes so as to disguise the truth from her carers. The nurses didn't cotton on to the fact that she wasn't actually urinating when she went to the toilet and her bruises returned with a vengeance before they could ban her from using the bathroom alone.

The first night Rosie and Alex came to visit, one of the girls tried to kill herself.

As they walked up the corridor to Jane's room, the girl was being rushed towards them. Bright red train tracks streamed out of the white paper towel that one of the nurses clenched around her wrists. There was a lot of blood and yelling and alarms going off. Alex was so distressed by it all that the next time he came to see his sister, he couldn't go to the communal toilet or family kitchen alone. He was scared he would see something like that again, so he used Jane's bathroom instead.

On their second visit, as they left, they were met with the wailing of an ambulance siren. Though they were on the road by the time the paramedics had entered the unit, Jane later told them that one of the patients had consumed so much water she had nearly drowned herself. Well, that was what the other girls had told her.

The girl had been refusing to gain weight for so long that the psychiatrist's threats of being sectioned had reached their climax. They had locked her bathroom door a while ago, to try and stop her from water loading, but she had made a deal with one of the other girls to fill up her water bottle in her bathroom in return for some laxatives that she had managed to sneak in. In her final attempt to deceive them, she had drunk so much liquid that her body thought it was drowning and she had almost, albeit accidentally, killed herself.

Their third visit (and Rosie and Alex's final), coincided with the simultaneous arrival of a new patient and, as they wheeled Jane down the corridor towards her room for some private family time, they could hear the ruckus of his screams,

'I'M GOING TO GET FAT.'
'I'M GOING TO KILL MYSELF.'

After that, Jane told them not to visit again. This was a cross that she didn't want her siblings to have to bear.

On Mum and Dad's eighth or ninth visit, Mum told Jane that she would give her a massage to relieve the aching in her joints. Jane was apprehensive. She knew that, if she got undressed, Mum would see the returned purple flushes, violent violets of shame, on her limbs. It would break Mum's heart.

The second she hesitated, Mum knew she was hiding something.

Jane could not deal with the guilt of eating as well as the guilt of hiding her self-harm so, with tentative motion, she stripped down to her underwear and Mum froze. Jane's lower spine was breaking through the skin and bleeding red sores pockmarked her back. Mum was not stupid. She could see that they correlated to the movement associated with a "crunch" or sit-up. The three hundred of them Jane had been doing every morning when she had twenty minutes of unobserved free time had made their presence known. After this revelation the privilege of less frequent observation, alongside the lock on Jane's bathroom door, was removed. Mum had marched straight out of her daughter's bedroom and right into the ward manager's office. The niceties of a knock were absent. His name was Paul.

Jane started her time in the inpatient unit with a female key nurse who she had begun working with when she was an outpatient. Jane struggled to open up to her and was rather relieved when she was told that Kate would no longer be designated to her. She was due to go on maternity leave. Kate's replacement was Marco.

Jane was wary of Marco because, for some reason unknown to her, she struggled to trust men. Marco had a very different way of going about things – he was a letter writer. After every conversation they would have, Marco would leave Jane a note under the door in her room or, if he was approaching the end of his shift and Jane was sleeping, would hand it over to the next nurse on Jane's observations. The notes were usually scribbled over two sides of A4 and laid out the reasons why Jane should be proud of what she had achieved that day. They never told her that she wasn't fat and they never told her that she wasn't ugly. They focused on Jane's worth beyond surface aesthetics – her intelligence, her inner strength and her attitude, rather than her face or body. They were light-hearted and they made Jane smile and laugh and cry, forcing her to reflect in ways that she wouldn't usually have done had she been left alone with her thoughts. They reinforced things that they had worked on during their sessions and they reminded Jane that she was capable of moments of lucid positive thought, even if they were few and far between.

The dining room was a small rectangular box that jutted off the back end of the unit. It was green – a brash neon sort of green - and housed four or five large, brightly coloured tables. The patients were grouped together in accordance with the zones they were in or their propensity for consuming solid over liquid nutrition. If a patient was at the end of their inpatient journey and could be trusted to eat alone, they would be sat on a table with other patients like them and the conversation would be rather less intense than that occurring amongst their fellow, Fortisip-fuelled patients at the opposite side of the room. Those patients sat at the table closest to the Fortisip fridges. The nurses knew that these children would refuse the solid food, but they still had to pretend that they believed in them and their ability to push through their guilt and eat the meals placed in front of them. Most of these patients tended to be in the "red" or "amber" zones and were on refeeding programs or wheelchair dependent like Jane.

When a new patient joined the ward, they would be encouraged to make themselves a placemat and decorate it with all of their own personal motivational factors to recover (and eat). One of the key nurses had done this for Jane in an act of kindness after her very first meal at the unit, She had taken every letter of her name and used it to start a sentence with one of Jane's goals or positive characteristics. It was on an orange piece of A3 paper with yellow foam letters and plastic jewels embellishing the compliments that littered the page. After a couple of sessions working with Jane and establishing the reasons why she wanted to get better, Marco put together a series of flashcards which he would read to her as she sat sobbing into an untouched bowl of branflakes.

Think of your family
Think of your friends
Think of university

Eating is normal
Everyone eats every day, it isn't just you
Food is fuel

You will be able to run again!
You will be able to go back to the vegetarian restaurant and work!
You will be able to go travelling!

When she would get nervous and start wringing her hands and pulling at her thighs, Marco would tell her to put her fingertips to her thumbs in turn and focus on the motion rather than the thoughts. It was easier said than done, but it would keep her hand preoccupied and was less of a trigger for the other patients on the same table who might have picked up Jane's flesh-squeezing habits if she wasn't careful.

Negative behaviours, toxic attitudes and irrational beliefs spread like wildfire in eating disorder inpatient units.

There would usually be two seats between one patient and another and a meal support worker would sit either opposite, or in-between them. The support worker would gently urge their charge to eat whatever was in front of them with words of encouragement, but never praise - praise or congratulations catalysed guilt. Marco was one of the "good" ones, because he would always eat the same meal that the patient had chosen from their prescribed list, rather than bringing in his own (seemingly healthier) snacks and packed lunch like some of his co-workers. For the girls that had those nurses or keyworkers, it made eating the meal they faced even more difficult, because they could see that the person in front of them was eating something that wasn't white and stodgy and carbohydrate heavy. This would make them feel even worse about what they were consuming and question the necessity of it all.

Capital FM would always be the soundtrack to their mealtimes. It would blare the 'UK Top 40' out on repeat throughout the day and Jane began to correspond every meal with a certain song. Though she was often more preoccupied with the vicious berating inside her head than the lyrics, occasionally one or two would stick out to her, 'I know that we are upside down' being one of them. Jane knew that what she was living was not normal. She knew that other seventeen-year-olds, just like her, were not sat next to a ten-year-old with a nasogastric tube tapping her feet in an anxious frenzy as she battled the bottle in front of her. She knew that they were probably spending their days getting drunk from mulled wine and eating mince pies, celebrating the holiday season in warm homes with warm hearts surrounded by people that they loved. They weren't staring ahead of them in a garish green room where silver tinsel dripped off doors without locks and plastic holly wreaths garnished windows that were constantly sealed so as to prevent patients from escaping.

Rosie and Alex were undoubtedly rather apprehensive about what Christmas would look like that year - they didn't expect it to be like any other they had celebrated in the past. Mum and Dad only wanted one thing - the same thing they had prayed for since the very first day they realised their daughter wasn't quite the same. They wanted their family, together, as one again, and Jane was the only one that could give them this gift.

Jane's world was far from normal - if there is such a thing – it was upside down, inside out, spinning around in an orbit that was so very un-normal it was almost laughable. A year ago she was kissing Toby behind a curtain, proud at the fact she had lost a little weight and excited to embark upon a free gym membership trial. Now? Now she was so severely malnourished that she had to have one-to-one supervision constantly and relied on a wheelchair in order to get her from one end of the corridor to the other. Her greatest fear was not failing to get a university offer or crashing her car on her driving test, it was food, and she knew that that in itself was intrinsically, and fundamentally, wrong.

The farewell text that Jane sent to the restaurant was not the only text she sent in the run up to Christmas that year. Zak fell victim to the second.

The fourth night that Jane spent in the inpatient unit was the night that Jane let her hero go. The hero who had told her he loved her less than two months earlier. It was a farewell that needed to happen but it didn't make it any easier to do. Jane drafted Zak a message. A long message. It explained that, despite loving him, she could not be with him anymore. She wasn't the same person he had fallen in love with and she could not be what she thought he deserved. Mum sat beside her as she typed. She told Jane that she should call him and have the conversation in person, but Jane could not bring herself to do it. Even at the age of seventeen, words, written or typed, were how she expressed herself most eloquently. Spoken words never really came out the way that she wanted them to. She loved Zak in a way which consumed her. It made her feel warm when she was eternally cold. He made her smile just by smiling himself and the ridiculous things that would come out of his mouth always managed to find a way to make her laugh. An honest laugh. One that made Mum and Dad's hearts happy when they heard it trickling out from underneath her bedroom door. Zak was a light in Jane's darkness. He was kind and good and true, but Jane couldn't bring him through the blackness with her. This was not his battle, it was hers and she had to set him free.

As the days tapered towards Christmas, Jane's weight slowly started to go up - constant observation leaves no room for deception. 100- 250g every four days was a miniscule amount, but enough to cause her paralysing guilt and catalyse some of the most physically exertive panic attacks of her life. The worst of these came two days before Jane was meant to go home on leave for Christmas day. It was the day that broke Jane, but the day that the very first jigsaw piece was placed into the frame of recovery.

It involved an act she was all too familiar with - she had done it a thousand times a day, every day, for seventeen years, eight months and fifteen days. Six thousand, four hundred and sixty-six days of the same unconscious action, but this time, it meant so much more than she could possibly ever know.

Jane swallowed.
A carrot, then two and then an entire Christmas dinner.

A singular gulp which would not only change her life, but seize it right back into her hands.

Jane's world had been upside down for months. This was the day it finally began to flip back around.

Chapter 8
The choice

Life exists as a spectrum. The people who occupy each pole are extreme in their distinction. At one end, there are those who pride themselves on their steady heads, on their happy lack of insane impulse, on no true desire for adventure or any act a little out of the ordinary. At the other, are individuals who act only on a whim – adrenaline junkies, chasing the highs of spontaneity that present themselves in the opportunities of the everyday or, extraordinary chances. The latter live their lives precariously balanced on the edge.

Jane lived life on the edge.

Sometimes, the biggest jumps involve the simplest of actions. Tiny choices with colossal consequences. Jane took a risk on the 23rd of December 2013. A risk with a domino effect that would, ultimately, change her life.

Jane ate a carrot and, in doing so, stepped off the edge.

* * *

She had not had "real" food since the morning of her admission.

Her psychiatrist had told her that the only way she would be able to spend Christmas with her family would be if she could prove that she was capable of managing solid food. This had to be prior to leave from the ward being arranged that evening. The evening of the 23rd.

Jane missed her opportunity at breakfast – an "easy" bowl of branflakes and a banana. She couldn't bring herself to do it. The first Fortisip of the day was ticked off her chart. Her morning snack should have been a Crunchie bar and a glass of apple juice. She couldn't bear the thought of chocolate. Down went Fortisip number two. Lunch came and went – her options were either a baked potato with cheese and beans or pasta – both white carbs and both "fear foods". Fortisip number three. Afternoon snack, another Fortisip and then, all of a sudden, she had one last chance.

Dinner.

Jane does not do things by halves; she is either "in" or "out" and, it was this all-or-nothing attitude, which found her crumpled at the dining table with a floppy paper crown and Mariah Carey singing on the radio at 17:03pm that evening.

The words that Rosie had written on an A4 piece of paper back in Jane's days in the paediatric wing suddenly floated to the forefront of her mind. 'God gives his hardest battles to his toughest soldiers.' Jane had lost her faith in a higher entity a long time ago, but, for some reason, today, these words particularly resonated with her.

17:04pm.
The ward manager, Paul, was designated as her meal support that day as Marco had been on the night shift the day before. Paul did not usually sit in the dining room with the patients – he was trained to be able to do so, but most of the time this was a role left for the key nurses and support workers. Jane was used to Marco. He would speak quietly to her, whisper for her to "settle" and, when she started squeezing the flesh on her thighs, he would encourage her to use the techniques that they had developed in their sessions to calm herself down.

Paul's approach was the exact opposite.

He made her feel guilty. He knew her hotspots when it came to family and aspirations and regaining her freedom. He manipulated them in a way that seemed almost malicious but, shockingly, it appeared to work.

Think about your family – if you love them that much why are you putting them through this? Do you not want to go back to school? What about university? Are you really going to throw all of this away because you can't pick up your fork? Christmas here in the unit, alone, is that what you want? You've brought this on yourself Jane - only YOU can change it. You can do it, but you have to TRY. You aren't even trying. This is down to you and you alone. Ignore her! She doesn't control you. Or does she?

17:05pm.
Jane was overcome with a feeling of anger. What Paul was saying was
true, but no one had said it in such a blunt and unapologetic way to her
before. Her rage stemmed from love. Both were feelings of red but one
was a soft, deep warmth and the other a violent heat. Her anger was a
red directed at herself for the pain she was causing. Red at all of the lies
she had told and all of the love she had stolen from Mum. Love that should
have been reserved for Rosie and Alex and Dad. Red at herself for letting
the boy she loved go and red at her body for refusing to nourish her for so
long. Red at her mind for its twisted beliefs and red at her eyes for failing to
see her body as it was. Jane did not only see red, she felt it and she used
the red that Paul had provoked to pick up her fork.

17:07pm.
She stabbed the least greasy looking carrot at the bottom of her plate.
Slowly, she lifted it and watched the light reflect off the oil. It looked almost
beautiful. It didn't smell as a carrot usually would, sweet earthiness. It smelt
like gravy. Everything smelt like gravy. Artificial onion "Bisto" glazing each
item in a congealing, brownish sheen. The little orange disc was just big
enough to cover the top of her thumb. She opened her mouth, ever so
slightly, and then she closed it again. She couldn't do it.
You've done the hardest part Jane. You've picked up the fork.
 Her lucid thoughts spoke gently to her, she knew that they were right.

Open.
You're a fat fuck Jane. WHAT ARE YOU DOING?! PUT IT DOWN! You're
useless and WEAK.
Anorexia reiterated with a vengeance.
Close.

She remembered Mum.
    Mum spoon-feeding her.
        Mum sleeping next to her.
            Mum holding her hand.
                Mum pushing her in her chair.
                Mum massaging her back.
                Mum wiping her tears.
                    Mum punching herself.

She opened her mouth and she put the carrot inside.

She let the other red win.

Her lips closed around the fork and she pulled it away leaving the carrot sat in the warm cavern of her mouth.

She let it rest there and she felt absolutely everything and absolutely nothing at the same time. Paul's voice and his pathetic attempts to encourage her were now no longer necessary. It was in her mouth. His cockney twang had buzzed into a monotonous hum and all of his guilt-tripping finally had an effect. He was almost as shocked as she was that she had actually done it.

She didn't hear him. All she heard was the pounding of her heart.

It thumped against the inside of her chest, drumming so hard she thought it might break through the bones that pressed close to her skin. She thought, what if it burst? A sudden explosion, a myriad of ruby droplets spraying across the table and dousing Paul, Christmas cracker crown and all, in ribbons of bloody muscle and matter.

It felt so foreign to her. Solid food.

She couldn't taste it. She didn't want to. All she could feel was fear and, for a moment, fear tasted like nothing. That is until anorexia reminded her that it tasted like fat.

17:11pm.
Jane swallowed.

As the little orange disc tumbled its way down from her tongue to her belly,
up
up
up
rumbled a tidal wave of something dark – something so grotesquely evil in its power that it crippled her.

But Jane could not sit back and let the paralysis – the guilt and shame and self-repulsion - consume her, because now she faced the hardest part. In swallowing the carrot – all ten calories of it – she had committed to the entire plate looming in front of her:
  turkey   and fat

and stuffing	and fat	
and pigs and blankets	and fat	
and potatoes	and fat	
and fat	and fat	**and fat.**

Every single morsel, fat.

She could not take it back. She could not say 'actually, no, I'll take the Fortisip-minus-ten-carrot-calories instead please'. It did not work like that. It was either food, Fortisip, or tube, and that was that.

Another carrot was stabbed and swallowed.

Two carrots consumed.

17:12pm.
With every bite she felt her thighs blubbering into lumpy trunks. Fat.

17:13pm.
With each gulp, her belly swelled, the fat depositing itself and making permanent rolls that she could picture almost as vividly as the gravy that slipped off her knife. Oily slickers.
FAT.

A quarter done.

17:15pm.
Mouthful by mouthful she tried to focus on the placemat - the words of a nurse she had only just met. She remembered the faces of her family and the sheet of A4 with Rosie's words on it:
Hold On Pain Ends – Lies.
If you have good thoughts they will shine out of your face like sunbeams and you will always look lovely – Lies.
You are beautiful– Lies.

The only thing she was, was a failure. She was FAT.

Halfway there.

17:20pm.
The pain felt like it was only getting worse with every swallow, every sob,

but she could not risk drinking the Fortisip instead – all six hundred calories of it – as well as "voluntarily" eating the solid food she had already gulped down. So, she kept on eating. By now the stream of salty tears and snot that gushed from her face made it all taste the same.

She was eating shame. Her shame.

One quarter left.

17:28pm.
Everyone at the table around her was silent. They watched her, nurses and patients alike, in utter awe.

The last roast potato.
17:30pm.
Jane placed the fork and knife down on her placemat. The nurse on duty called 'time' but Jane could only hear her heartbeat. She couldn't see. Everything was foggy and she felt hot.

17:32pm.
There wasn't a single patient left in the room. They had all elected to drink their supplement, rather than eat the food, and had been ushered out as quickly as possible after 'time' was called. The only person left was Paul. His plate was also empty, but, instead of guilt colouring the pallor of his face white, it was the red flush of nervous heat. He did not know what to expect as Jane placed the cutlery down. He had watched her in stunned silence, but now something was radically wrong. The look in her eyes said it all.

She was still.

That was the first sign of something brewing. Usually, Jane would be constantly tapping her feet up and down and up and down or pressing her fingers together to distract her from the act that she had just committed. Committed like a sin. Eating was a sin.
In anorexia's eyes at least.

He knew she was capable of great self-harm and he knew that the usual post-Fortisip guilt would be a hundred times worse after eating solid food.

The same stillness washed over Jane as it had the day she was admitted to the unit. The day she sat on the toilet and said goodbye to her freedom in the flushing of the chain.

The stillness lasted longer – around three minutes and, in her momentary loss of sight, Jane saw clearly her mother's face. She was smiling.

This time, the stillness meant something different.
It meant freedom.
It meant that she had proved herself capable.
She had eaten solid food. Not just any solid food, an entire Christmas dinner. In doing so, she had taken a leap of faith so big and so bold and so blind, that it might just end up saving her life.

Then the moment stopped.
Reality hit her in its most brutal and unkind way. With the wave of realisation, her sight returned and the blurry white disc in front of her suddenly found a focus. It was empty. All of that food was inside of her and she could feel it. Every last morsel.

'Jane, let's go and take a seat in the therapy room, hey?'
Paul was nervous.

Jane nodded slowly and slid her chair backwards. From one seat to another, she sat down in her wheelchair and Paul took her up the corridor into Therapy Room 1. Kathy, Jane's favourite nurse, joined them and, as soon as the door closed behind them, the hysterics were released.

All of the thoughts that Jane had had over the last year:
       the self-hatred, the regret, the guilt,
       her fears, her hopes, her dreams,
       anorexia's beratements and Jane's encouragements,
       words spoken by voices inside and outside of her head,
       the punching, the exercising, the crying,
       the red, the blue, the black, washed over her.

They had consumed her in their own unique ways for months but now they hit her all at once and, in her hour-long catharsis, she wept through them all.

Afterwards, once she had cried till she could cry no more and her head was dizzy with dehydration, she slept. The best she had slept in a very long time. The physical and mental exertion had taken it out of her. For the first time in months, she could rest easy. She knew that tomorrow was Christmas Eve and, by some form of magic, she was going to be able to spend it with her family at home.

Brave is not a word Jane would ever use to describe herself, but brave is what she was.

* * *

After Christmas, Jane faced a ferocious fight for recovery, but she had taken the hardest step; she could now consume solid food. Her guilt was still crippling, but with the painstakingly slow increase of weight came the nourishment she needed to enable her cognitive function to improve. With food came a mounting ability to rationalise. Jane was regaining control and developing ways to manage the guilt, rather than letting it overwhelm her.

After Christmas day, Jane returned to the ward with a new sense of positivity. She had experienced time spent at home that wasn't entirely traumatic. Yes, Christmas dinner had been just as hideously challenging as the one she had consumed two days before in the ward, but this time, instead of fellow patients and nurses surrounding her, it was her family. These were people she knew wouldn't judge her and people that only wanted one thing, for her to get better. Mum weighed everything out exactly so that Jane could see what she was going to be faced with. She didn't put any seasoning on or add any butter or fat and, when it came to eating, she sat beside her and squeezed her hand under the table as, slowly but surely, Jane picked up her cutlery and fought her way through the meal in front of her.

Mum and Dad couldn't believe what they were seeing, but they didn't say a word. Mum knew that telling her that they were proud of her would just trigger Jane's guilt. If she remained silent, saying all that she needed to say in the squeezing of her hand, Jane could focus on the guilt stemming from the sensation of a full stomach, rather than the additional regret at the act of eating itself.

It was a rather simple Christmas that year.

Mum and Dad couldn't afford much. Their savings had been spent, long before Christmas, in order to fund the practical side of caring for a child with a severe eating disorder. Though the material worth of this particular Christmas was lessened, the emotional gratitude and appreciation for family, magnified exponentially. There was no need for physical restraint, no self-harm, no "secret" exercise. Jane had kicked some of her most debilitating habits and it was the greatest gift that she could have given to her mother – and to her family.

Soon enough, New Year's Eve came around and Dr E was so impressed with Jane's efforts since Christmas that she granted her leave again. Her parents asked her how she wanted to see 2014 in. She told them that she wanted to spend it with them - doing the things that she loved with the people that she loved. Just the five of them. It had been nearly four months since Jane had been to visit her favourite place in the North East, The Reservoir. That was where she had decided that they would leave 2013 behind.

After an evening spent playing hide and seek in the dark and various other games, the five of them jumped into the car and drove to The Reservoir, just in time for midnight. They sat on the wall and watched the moon reflect off of the stillness of the water. Jane breathed in air that felt so much cleaner than the musty heat of the constantly hot ward. Dad popped open a bottle of Prosecco and they all took a glass. Jane sipped hers and then threw the rest over her shoulder when no-one was looking. Yes, she was in recovery, but she was not ready to consume "unnecessary" additional calories just yet. A singular sip was a success in itself.

They welcomed in the year, perched on a stone wall in the most peaceful and beautiful place they possibly could. Silent in their shared happiness and in their hope. They "cheers-ed" to a better year, the year of Jane, not of anorexia. The year of family and the year of memoires carved out of love, rather than hatred and deceit. If they could have known just exactly how much greater 2014 would be, they would have cried with the relief of it all. Their family had been through an ordeal which no family should ever have to go through and Jane knew that something was about to change.

They all did.

An unspoken anticipation for life no longer ruled by anorexia. The silent dictator of 2013.

Chapter 9
The Little Red Balloon

The next three years of Jane's life happened.
That's just it. They happened.

A series of stolen moments. Vignettes perhaps. Memories of a period of three years which was blissfully unmemorable, because there was no anorexia really. Merely life.

This chapter recalls some of these moments.

Little stories about little things that Jane remembers from 2014 to 2017. Moments of life and recovery and hope. Moments of love. Moments of a normal girl doing normal things like attending university and sitting exams. Moments like making porridge for breakfast and ordering coffee from the Students' Union, hungover. Moments like pot-lucks for dinner and taking pictures with a polaroid. Moments of fairy-lit ceilings in Student Accommodation and catching the Northern Lights over the Pier. Moments of Birthdays and Christmases and Easters spent playing football with cousins. Moments of tears and moments of laughter. Moments of burnt, salty sesame potatoes dipped in left-over butterscotch sauce at the end of a shift. Moments of firsts – cigarettes, clubs and camping. Moments of manies – drives home for Christmas, hysterics in the mirror and splitting Sunday morning headaches. Moments worth mentioning, moments that are not. Moments that were forgotten before they were even lived. Mundane, memorable, multifaceted, monochromatic moments.

Moments that are just that. Momentary.
Why? Because this was a life, Jane's life, which was far too busy being lived to be remembered.

Jane had been given another chance, another shot, and so she made the most of it. It was not without its hurdles, but it was living. It was recovery.

Until, it wasn't. But we shall get to that in due course.

Anorexia does not go away. Recovery does not clear the cancer. It remains, in spores. Sometimes clustering into persistent thought and focus. Sometimes blowing quietly into the everyday. The eating disorder was always present in the back of Jane's mind, but other things filled the space it had dominated for so long. Food was fuel and fuel was what was needed for life to happen. Recovery enabled Jane to see this. It enabled Jane to let the promise of living supersede the desire to be skinny. To be 'anorexic'.

Over the next three years, there was never a point when Jane did not fear weight gain, but she learnt to manage that fear. She learnt to prioritise other things. Things that involved letting go of the voice – sometimes. Letting go of that desire to constantly control – sometimes. Letting go of the fear of letting go – sometimes. Her weight fluctuated, not noticeably to others, but to herself. When it happened, she would wobble a little and then, reset. She developed coping mechanisms: lists of the calories she had consumed. Trying certain diets – vegan, vegetarian, gluten-free. But she always seemed to find her way back to something resembling normality. Some form of dietary existence that enabled her to do the things she wanted to without the guilt clouding every day. She balanced. Rather precariously at times, but tiptoed along the tightrope with success. Never slipping too far to be unable to pull it back. Had she fallen, she had the means to stand back up again. Family, friends and people who could help her. People who only ever wanted to see her thrive. These people, Jane's 'People', kept her alive and, preoccupying herself with them helped her switch her focus to the living part of life, rather than the fearing. People, pain and love. People and love made Jane's recovery possible. Pain is what ultimately caused her fall. But the fall is another matter for another time. For now, let us talk about the good stuff. The flight of the Little Red Balloon.

C.A.T – Cognitive Analytical Therapy
When Jane was finally capable of thinking lucidly, Dr. E began a course of C.A.T. with her. Most of the other patients in the ward followed a C.B.T program, but, due to the nature of Jane's eating disorder, Dr. E had though that C.A.T seemed more appropriate.

Even when Jane was an outpatient, before the debacle of Ward 13, the doctors had always been somewhat baffled at the state of her mind. Her thoughts and behaviours were intensely self-deprecating and self-destructive. They didn't seem to match the physical state of her body. It was something that had made treating Jane's mental illness a lot more difficult, because, physically, she was not deemed "sick" enough to receive the appropriate medical care and support. Care and support that her mind desperately needed.

That was until her body finally caught up with her mind and her organs began shutting themselves down.

The main difference between C.A.T and C.B.T was that C.A.T involved trying to find the core of Jane's problems, forcing her to address how they might resolve certain thought patterns, attitudes and beliefs that had become cemented in her everyday existence. It also involved a lot of drawing and so Dr. E gave Jane a lot of paper.

Whenever she would describe herself, her thoughts or her feelings, Dr.E encouraged her to draw them so that she might also visualise them. Jane would do so under the guise of a little red balloon. The Little Red Balloon. A little red balloon that would float upwards, from a crying stickman sitting on a ledge, through a glass ceiling and up up up into something brighter. A future that Jane was desperate to make the present.

Their sessions continued after Jane was discharged - in March 2014. Her last appointment was the week before she left for university. Dr. E wrote her a letter telling her how proud she was of the work that Jane had put in and how excited she was for her to start this new chapter of her life. Jane had written back, thanking her for everything. She had put it in a card. One she had made herself. A card and a silk scarf to attempt a thank you that money could not possibly ever buy. Dr. E was the first professional not to give up on Jane. Many people had and many people would continue to do so, but not Dr. E. Dr. E with her perfectly set hair and her dark rimmed spectacles. A woman with immaculately folded scarves and suits that looked as if they had come right off of a rack in Marks and Spencer's that morning. Dr. E helped Jane realise the beauty of the potential in existing free from self-doubt and free from self-deprecation. Though their paths only ever crossed in an icy portacabin somewhere in the midst of a red-bricked council estate for just under a year, Dr. E was a person, one of Jane's 'People', that made it possible for Jane's story to be written.

It takes a village (or a ward...)
Jane had grown to love her fellow patients – absurd behaviours and all – and she had learnt new things about them every day.

She knew which side of the table Amanda had to sit on so that her O.C.D did not make the task of eating any more difficult than it already was. She knew that Bea had every stuffed sea creature under the sun piled up on her bed, but that she was missing a small blue turtle. She bought her one and together they called it Steve. She knew that Bethan never used the wheelchair when she was on leave – she had seen her walking in from the car park, making the most of the steps while she had the freedom to do so. Her parents had stopped trying to fight her after her first admission, and her second. Bethan was ill- very, very ill. She'd been in CAMHS since she was eleven.

She knew that Ellie hated Dr.E. and that there wasn't a single good thing that the girl had to say about her. Jane soon realised it was best to take everything Ellie told her with a pinch of salt - or two – for she was quite the story-teller and exacerbation was her ink.

She knew precisely what to say (and what not to say) to Jake. He was a tempest of a boy with some form of mild Tourette's. It meant he said exactly what he thought and, in an environment where everybody's thoughts were mainly the same recurring fear of 'I'm going to get fat', it was not the most conducive of character traits. Especially when it was yelled across the living room, every day after breakfast.

 She knew that Chloe was a dancer and that she loved her brother and sister dearly. Just like Jane. She was quiet and anxious but one of the most sensitive and caring girls in there.
She knew that Dorothy experienced a lot of physical pain - self-inflicted and genetic. She had to be particularly careful when she hugged her because even the slightest squeeze could cause her bouts of extreme agony.

She knew that Tia and Rebecca wanted to get better. That their eating disorders were less body-image based and more a coping mechanism for dealing with other trauma in their lives. It seemed ludicrous, even to Jane with her illogical mind, but Rebecca had just forgotten how to eat. Literally, forgotten. And Tia? Tia had an insatiable hunger, one she had created through extreme athleticism that she simply hadn't had the time to satisfy.

She knew that Liza had other issues, things that were separate to her eating disorder. Things that were even darker and even more harmful. Mental illness is a cancer that likes a friend. Sometimes many.

She knew that lots of the girls couldn't wear nail varnish because they were scared that there were calories in the paint. Calories that would absorb into their skin.

She knew that they held their breath when they baked cakes in Occupational Therapy sessions in case they accidentally inhaled some of the icing sugar that clouded from box to bowl. She knew that they always chose the most fattening recipes because they wouldn't be the ones eating the cakes – that was the responsibility of the nurses.
Anorexia is a feeder. Just not to the body it occupies.

She knew that every single one of them was a liar but that the biggest victim of their lies was themselves.

She knew that they knew that their actions were completely logically skewed, but that they were not in control of them and she knew this because she was one of them. No matter how well she fuelled her body or how deeply challenged her mind, she always would be.

But it did not stop her trying.

Because of her love for them and her hope for their survival, for their "lightbulb" moment, she took it upon herself to provide the meal support that some of the nurses seemed to give up on far too easily. Where the odd support worker would stop encouraging their charge after five minutes of half-arsed 'you-can-do-it's' and 'think-of-your-family's', Jane would push the patients next to her to the very last minute. Telling them that the 'guilt would pass' and that 'food was fuel' till, eventually, one day they started to listen.

Jane's recovery was not just her own, it was theirs and her passion and desire to start a life free of anorexia was inspiring to them. They loved her, just as she loved them and they wanted what she promised– the bliss of rational thinking and the prospect of a real future.

When Jane left Ward 13, she did not thank her fellow inpatients with silk scarves and cards. Instead, she named a star after them.

Trust
With time, Jane was deemed stable enough to be trusted not to hurt herself.
She regained control in a healthy way and she refused to let her renewed
freedom lead her to slip back into old habits.

She remembered how to be independent and she loved it.

She washed her own hair with her own hands - not Mum's – with shampoo
that smelt like coconut. She took pleasure in letting the hot water run over
her face, allowing the moment to be a moment and not one where she felt
she had to fill the empty minutes with additional jogging on the spot, or
sit ups. Her desperate attempts to remove the guilt from being temporarily
stationary were now mere echoes. Echoes left in an empty room, in a ward
that she had outgrown. Showering was a thing to be enjoyed, not a time
to punish herself and, with this change of perspective, she proved that she
could be allowed to use the bathroom without having to be monitored. The
bruises on her spine began to heal and the scars that marked the places
where her bones had broken through the skin formed the atlas of her
recovery. Lines that she would learn to love for their significance, rather
than the haunting memory of desperation. She realised she didn't want to
be cold all of the time, so she closed her window and she allowed herself
to indulge in the art of rest without requirement – she sat when she didn't
have to and she slept soundly. The alarms and alerts she had scheduled to
start the day on only four hours of sleep were now absent. The rigmarole of
toxic routine, the musts and shoulds and needs had been lost in the past.

After four months, she no longer relied on the wheelchair.

The morning after the weigh-in which confirmed it, she cried.
For the first time in a very long time, they were not tears of sadness, they
were tears of joy.

It would be wrong to say that the reality of the numbers did not initially
trigger a wave of self-hatred, but then Jane looked up to the drawing on
the wall.
'No scale can measure how much we are loved or how incredibly precious
we are'

She took a deep breath.
She was far from loving her body, but the reprieve her parents would feel
and the happiness she knew that this would bring would make this moment

worth it, even if it meant the thing she still feared the most - weight gain. Jane's fears no longer defined her. They still existed, she was still human, but she was getting better at processing and accepting that. Yes, she experienced them alongside the guilt, six times a day before and after every meal, but she was now capable of distracting herself. Though there were days when she didn't feel strong enough to ride the wave, days when she would find herself flailing around in the surf, those days were getting fewer and fewer. The good moments made it feel worthwhile.

Discharge
The day Jane was discharged was a good day but a day she cannot quite remember.
Perhaps there were celebrations, perhaps there were not.
Sometimes it's the biggest things we forget to make big.

The precise date, the clothes she was wearing, the time of departure – they are all blurs to Jane. Little details she wishes she could remember, but details her subconscious brain decided just were not necessary. They did not quite make the cut for the place where memorable moments tend to collect.

If she were to ask Mum and Dad to recall those very same specific details, she can guarantee they also would not remember. The day Jane was discharged was too full of joy for the facts to be a focus. All that they know was that it was a day, sometime in March, and that it was a good day. The first really good day, in a really long time.

Change is good
Though Discharge Day was just another day to Jane, the following was somewhat more memorable. It was the day she cut off all of her hair.

She had been thinking about it for a while but, having been obsessed with having a "chubby" face, it wasn't a look she thought she could pull off. However, as is the case with all subconscious thoughts, there comes a time when an idea – no matter how deeply buried – becomes persistent. Too persistent to ignore. Jane had decided that all fresh starts must begin with a change, a physical change at that. This time, she chose her hair.

In the past she had got piercings. Her ears were her way of "expressing herself" but, for some reason unbeknown to her, discharge from an inpatient eating disorder unit called for something a little more drastic

– a little more permanent.

She sat on the chair in the hairdressers. She was excited. This was something new, something fresh. Her adrenaline and thirst for change were shared by everyone in the salon around her. When she was happy, Jane was infectious. A little tornado. People were magnetised to her energy. They couldn't help it. Strangers, or not.

When she left the salon, Jane felt more like herself than she had in a long time. People stopped and stared at her petite elfin face on the street. She had thought it was her hair – the bold new trim. In reality, it was the brightness that shone through her eyes. Big, brown irises that were all of a sudden, animated. Animated and happy and alive.
Birthdays
Jane's eighteenth birthday came around on the 10th of April and she was desperate to celebrate.

Mum and Dad wanted to do anything and everything to make the most of the last few months they had with their daughter before she headed off to university (results pending) and so, they agreed to allowing her whatever birthday celebration she desired.

Mum bought her an ice-cream cake from the ice-cream parlour in town. It had a little pink butterfly on it and was something Jane had always wanted to try since she saw it in the window an eternity ago. Before anorexia. Back when ice-cream was allowed.

They went shopping and Jane picked out a rather daring jumpsuit in red. Real red kind of red. With her cropped black hair and her (almost) absurdly large eyes, she looked striking. When the day of the party came, Mum caught her breath.

This time, it was not because her daughter's naked skeleton stood crouched and bruised and shaking before her. It was because here was her little girl. Her little Jane. All grown up. All bold and beautiful in red. She was not a girl anymore. She was a woman.

When a mother looks at her daughter, she sees a part of herself. Right there, at the very heart of her child.

When a mother looks at a girl, her girl, all she wants to do is protect and hold and nurture and love. A little, sweet, precious piece of herself that is also physically separate from her. Though a girl is dependent on her mother for eighteen years, a mother's desire to protect so that no harm will ever come to her daughter is intrinsic – it goes beyond the contract of childhood.

When a mother looks at a woman, her woman, it is with an unflinching sense of pride. Maternal pride. Something which cannot be taught and something which cannot be bought. Maternal pride is instinctive – it comes with being a mother - and, when Jane's mother looked at her daughter, the day that she became an adult, her heart filled with an unparalleled sense of love. The little girl who had battled through such intense psychological trauma over the past eighteen months was now a woman. Mum couldn't help but find herself winded with the magnitude of it all.

The next year, Jane's nineteenth birthday, was memorably unmemorable. She spent it at university in Halls, very, very drunk. A red fez was passed around, a blue Hollister skirt with little white embroidered flowers was worn. Guinness Cake was made by Jane's best friend, Ophelia, and devoured. Candles were blown out. The next day was one spent hung over. Very hung over.

The year after that, Jane's twentieth birthday, involved a BBQ and a rather unfortunate bowl of poorly mixed salad dressing. This had been Jane's flatmate's responsibility and he had over-mustarded the balsamic glaze. Zak had visited Jane in Halls the night before. They had attended a Ball and Jane had worn a short tartan dress and black heels. She had straightened her hair, finally at shoulder length after the big chop of 2014. It had been one of the best nights she had had at university so far. They had eaten 'drunk food' on their walk home, ceilidh-ed till her feet had bled and Zak had met her at the venue with a bouquet of lilies. Jane's favourite.

Relationships
When Jane left for university in September, Alex bought her a copy of 'Guess How Much I Love You' and in the front of it he wrote:

A message from Alex to Jane 2014

Dear Jane,
I am a very unlucky person to only have known you since you were four.
I wish I could have those extra four years with you.

We had our good times, and bad, and my biggest regret is standing against you so often.
I love you so much!
Keep in touch and have a good time.
If you need anything please call me.
I love you all the way to the moon and back.

Your loving brother
Alex.
xxxxxxxxxx
P.S. I love you

Alex was fourteen.

Rosie put together a photo album for her. Pictures of them sitting in a bathtub as babies or cooking at their miniature play kitchen. "Selfies" from their first night out together when they were a little older and family snaps of the five of them at Warner Bros Studies in London - the day their childhood dreams came true and they walked along Privet Drive. Rosie's note read;

A message from Rosie to Jane 2014

Wow... I don't even know where to start Jane. Obviously, this year's been huge for us and amongst other things really strengthened our relationship. However, I would like to point out that you've always been my best friend since day one, undeniably you've driven me crazy a fair few times but I wouldn't change you for the world. You constantly inspire me Jane, I want to be as incredible as you are when I leave home and can only dream of having as much love in my heart as you do. You're my guardian angel; Always there for me when I need you the most and persist in filling me with confidence endlessly. Words cannot describe how much I'm going to miss not having you around but you're a star and you need to shine. I love you all the world Jane you're my rock and my inspiration and while I'm leaving my best friend, Scotland is gaining a national treasure. Love you forever and always.
Budlia xxx

Rosie was sixteen.

Rosie and Alex had lost their sister. She had abandoned them - with no warning - for a different playmate – the voice inside her head. But, as Jane grew stronger, she made her return, as their sister. She made a promise to herself that never again, would she make them feel like they didn't have a sister anymore.

Zak and Jane had rekindled their relationship after Jane was discharged. It had been Grandad Peter's birthday and he had come by to see the family and wish Grandad well. As the two of them had brought the cake through from the kitchen, Jane had leaned behind her and kissed him. It had been simple but, just like that, the past was in the past.

Zak loved Jane, no matter what her shape or size.

He loved her for her spirit and her feisty attitude, both of which returned to her face in the same blush of life. His encouragement was paramount in enabling Jane to start accepting her new body and its healing, for he had always loved the curves that she had been so terrified of – the curves that manifested themselves in the unforgiving, hormonally-imbalanced, maelstrom of puberty. Her acceptance that they were not something she should be ashamed of and realisation that an eighteen-year-old woman with the body shape of a twelve-year-old girl was not in the least bit attractive, enabled the barricades of her self-consciousness to begin to disintegrate. She allowed him to see her body, in all of its scarred and fragile beauty, but she also began to trust him enough to let him show her how much he physically loved it too.

Growth

When she was at her worst, Jane had regressed into a toddler. Not only in mind, but in body. Her reliance on liquid nutrition, the need to be monitored at all hours of the day, an inability to be mobile unless being pushed around in a wheelchair et cetera et cetera. She had become a spoon-fed, hand holding, dependent waif of a thing.

Jane grew into a woman with the same series of firsts.

She taught herself how to walk. Love for her family let her take that first step.

Her love of learning – one that was finally absent of the self-inflicted pressure for high achievement that she had heaped upon herself in earlier days – allowed her to keep up the pace of her stride for recovery. She knew that her grades were best when she wasn't starving herself, when

she was nourishing her body and her mind so that she could unlock the full potential of her analytical brain. So, she did what needed to be done in order for her to succeed.
She ate.

One morning, in early March, Mum sat Jane down and said to her, 'It's time to make a choice.' 'What do you mean Mum?'
'I mean that whatever you do, whatever you choose, we will support you. We only want the best for you. You know that, right? Your recovery is all that matters.'
'I know, I know. Go, on.'
'Ok, well, depending on your choice, on what you choose, we need to make some decisions so that we can help you get to the stage you want to be at.'
'You're talking about Uni right?'
'Mhmm'
'I'm going, Mum. She's not taking any more time from me. I swear. I'm going.'

And she did.

University
Jane and her parents made plans to visit the universities that had offered her a place. Bristol and St Andrews. Bristol was big and busy and full of people. As a city, it excited and intimidated Jane in equal measure. St Andrews was the very opposite - a little seaside town on the north eastern coast of Scotland. It was a place that smelt like the sea. She knew that it was home, almost immediately. She felt it before she lived it. St Andrews held the promise of something extraordinary and Jane knew that extraordinary was exactly what she needed.

She committed to grasping it.

She started to spend time with a Chemistry tutor. She taught herself the entire A-Level history syllabus in three months. She met with her English tutor on Thursday afternoons to go through coursework and trial examination questions. The challenge of intellectual exertion – something she had not been able to indulge in for months due to her previously malnourished mind – possessed her.

When her A-level results were handed to her in a brown paper envelope in August, she couldn't believe the reality that she had actually managed to pull her future right back into her hands; a future which had seemed so unattainable mere months before: A, A*, A* and a confirmed place to study English Literature at the University of St Andrews – the dream was now a reality and her hunger for its beginning was insatiable.

Travel

The next three years saw Jane embark upon many European adventures. She interrailed the summer before university: Amsterdam, Berlin, Prague, Vienna, Rome, Parma and Valencia. In Vienna, they went to a club. There was a bouncer outside who thought Jane looked like Helena Bonham Carter.

* * *

'Oi! Excuse me!'

Jane was startled and somewhat terrified. She did not speak Czech.
'What does he want?', she whispered to Kane.
Kane shrugged. 'I dunno, just go over and see what he wants. I'm right behind you ok?'
Kane was not the most strapping of eighteen-year-olds, but Jane appreciated his back-up, nonetheless.
She shuffled over to the man in black. He was big and rather scary looking and she could not see his eyes because of the tint in his glasses.
Jane had no idea what he was saying. He pulled out his phone and pointed to Jane and then to his screen.
'You' then, 'look like' a gesture to a YouTube video.
It was 'Fight Club'.
Jane laughed, so did the bouncer. It was a compliment, one she was willing to take.

* * *

In her first year at St Andrews, Jane competed in a charity hitchhike to Madrid. She finished the final stretch in a travelling theatre troop's van. They were friendly folk and they gave her and her fellow travellers blankets and tea. It was an experience that left her exhausted and dirty but with a renewed appreciation for the good to be found in strangers and a love for the city of Madrid. She went back the next year with Zak.
A city is a place that can be experienced many ways: with someone

you love, alone, at night, during the daytime, et cetera et cetera. Jane experienced it "in love" and "in extreme sleep-deprivation". Both were unique experiences and both instilled a closeness for Spain's capital that she continued to nurture for many years to come.

Jobs

Over the next three years, Jane worked a lot. She worked at a smoothie bar. She worked as a nanny. She wrote for university magazines and she trained to be a barista. She learned the trade of being a chef and she created her own bakery business. Part-time work kept her mind busy and she met some remarkable people as a result.

There was never a point in her life that she was not working because work gave her a purpose outside of her studies. She loved her degree but she loved the fast pace of the hospitality industry more. The people she met – locals and students alike – became the sort of easy-friendships that might sustain a person. A person whose self-worth was still very much determined by other peoples' opinions of her. It was why Jane often struggled to say no. No to extra shifts or no to staying back late. It was a mantra which extended into her relationship with Zak and one which made her extremely tired when it came to travelling to and from Dundee (where Zak was studying) after long hours in the café, or smoothie bar, or preoccupying young children.

* * *

'You couldn't do me a massive favour and stay till close could you J? Layla called in sick...again.'
A quick assessment of her deadlines that week. Essay due Friday but no class till Tuesday.
'Sure! No worries at all!'
'Oh, thank you! You are a superstar.'

A moment revelling in the compliment. Then, realisation she would have to leave for Dundee two hours later meaning dinner would be delayed which would mean she would be eating later than she usually did which would mean she would be bloated by the time they went to bed which would mean she wouldn't want Zak to touch her tummy which would need some form of explanation which she really did not have.
A "to and a fro" between her options.

1.   Text Zak and tell him she couldn't make it over tonight
2.   Tell Tara she actually could not stay after all

Option 1 meant she could make a little extra money, get brownie points from Tara and go for a run after work.

Option 2 meant she could see Zak and Zak was busy this weekend and so today was the only day she could see him.

'The "Mango Monkey"? Sure! That'll be 6.80 for a large.'
The till zipped out and she pulled out £3.20.

There was an option 3. Work the shift and tell Zak she would be over later, but that she would eat before she came. Grab something on her way. Something that wouldn't make her bloat. Maybe nothing at all – then she would feel sexy. Hungry, but sexy. Powerful but hungry.

* * *

More often than not, option 3 was Jane's final choice. Option 3 led to the development of toxic patterns of behaviour and Jane's mind was good at latching onto those. It made it increasingly difficult for her to eat around other people, not just Zak, but Ophelia and her flatmates. It made food something she ate on the go or when she was alone. Food became something she controlled, again. It made her feel powerful, again. Powerful knowing that she chose what went in and what didn't. She stopped socialising because it was not just Zak she was afraid of seeing her bloated, but all of her friends. It meant she spent her evenings in her room, eating the food she craved, because she did not have to worry about the unexpected calories that came from drinking or pot-luck dinners. She watched a lot of Netflix and ate a lot of food that came out of jars – the kitchen was a social space and social spaces started to terrify her. Work was the only place where she interacted with people and soon the easy-friendships became her only friendships and they were not even really friendships at all.

Chapter 10
Relapse

In 2017, Jane relapsed. Recovery is not plain sailing.

Just as love can be a person's saviour, it may also be their downfall.

Three years after her discharge from Ward 13, Jane found herself sitting
in her car outside the gym on a cold March afternoon, somewhere on the
outskirts of Dundee. She was crying into her phone. Mum was on the other
end of the call. There was no talking, just sobbing.

Eventually, Mum broke the silence.
'Jane? Talk to me sweetheart, what's going on?'
She asked the obvious, as all good Mums do, but she knew. She had done
for a while, but she had wanted to believe Jane when she had told her that
she was fine.
Desperately.
There was silence. Mum could hear the gentle thud of the windscreen
wipers beating back the rain.

'Jane, love? Talk to me.'
...
'I can't do it anymore, Mum.'
And down the balloon fell.

There are many different ways the conversation could have then gone.
Mum could have said,
'Yes, you can. You've done it before and you will do it again.'
The can-do-will-do approach.

She could have said,
'I know sweetheart, I know. Come home.'

The I-see-you-and-I-hear-you approach.

She could have said,
'Can't do what Jane?'
The I-refuse-to-accept-this-is-happening-again approach.

But instead she said,
'We can.'
Because Mum and Jane were a team and Mum needed to remind her daughter that this wasn't about 'I', this was about 'them'.

'We can' Mum said.
'We' Jane whispered.
'We' Mum said.

It took hitting rock bottom, again, but Jane knew its ground like the back of her hand. The last three years had been memorably unmemorable, but, amidst the mundanity, something had started to slip and, as Jane had lost control, anorexia had gained it.
* * *

The past three years had been full of firsts and a life that wasn't wholly determined by calories, exercise and weight. It had been three years spent with Zak.

 Zak and Jane had moved to Scotland with two very bright, but very different futures ahead of them. Though they had tried to make things work, Zak had fallen out of love with Jane and Jane had found solace in the arms of anorexia. A lover whose affection was starvation.

They had made some extraordinary memories, Zak and Jane.

In Madrid, they had eaten tapas and drunk coffee that tasted like chocolate. In Dublin, they had drunk Guinness, watched The Lumineers play live in an old theatre and danced to the acoustic magic of local musicians in the Temple Bar. In Dundee, they had eaten brunch and had drunk skinny cappuccinos in nearly every café.

They had danced their way through pubs and clubs and waltzed in the kitchen of Zak's student accommodation, whilst blitzing strawberry daiquiris. They had squeezed into his (and her) single bed with no complaint or qualm and when Zak had finally upgraded to a double bed, they had revelled in the luxury. They had spent many weekends lazing around in Zak's room, playing James Bay's classics on his guitar and, on the rare weekday that Jane would spend in Dundee, they had made enough lasagne for dinner to feed a small army. They had worked out together at the gym and, on Sundays, had run across the Tay Bridge. After exercise, they had consumed every calorie that they had burnt in hauls of Kinder Bueno and Ben and Jerry's. They were known for late Friday night Tesco runs in stripey pyjama bottoms and St Andrews Hockey shirts.

Zak knew Jane didn't have a normal relationship with food, but when she was around him, she didn't feel like she had to try as hard to disguise it. He had been there through it all and he knew that every "cheat day" they had, wasn't something she accepted or engaged in easily. He appreciated her trying but, increasingly often, he found himself wishing for something resembling a little more normal - a girlfriend that would eat the "peri-peri fries" at Nando's, rather than just the "macho peas".

Zak was a thinker and Jane was a dreamer, but all dreamers and thinkers dabble in one another's' trades on occasion. Usually, when Jane and Zak crossed intellectual paths, it would be over the likes of Oscar Wilde or T.S. Eliot.

Every car journey would have its own soundtrack – more often than not featuring a large amount of Drake. They had been some of Jane's favourite moments, because she was reminded of a life that existed before Zak became adult-Zak. Back when he was a kid, just like Jane, and the many distractions of university life hadn't got in the way. She would feel the palm of his hand on her knee and it would bring her comfort – everything was OK as long as she could feel his heat, his warmth, his touch – but then that gesture of simple love became less and less frequent and, in its absence, a profound coldness and loneliness took its place.

They had broken up, many times, but as old flames tend to, they had always seemed to find their way back to one another. Whether it be at a "Class of 2014" school reunion or in the foyer of the gym they used to call their second home. Again, and again, Jane had found herself in Dundee, making excuses to text him or bump into him at the library. Her best friend had become his flatmate's ex-girlfriend and they would go on nights out in the hope that he would be there too. When he did see her, they had gone home together, but there had been many nights she had slept at Marianne's and those nights had ended in tears and cigarettes.

After Christmas 2016, Zak had made it clear that he didn't want the label of a relationship but that he did want the "exclusivity" of it. He didn't want to share Jane with anyone else, but he still enjoyed the game. She didn't have eyes for anyone but him. For Jane, there was no game to be played.

She was besotted, but he no longer was. She could see his body language changing towards her – he was more closed off - but she was in love with him and so she refused to address it.

Mum had observed her daughter from afar. Nearly two-hundred-and-fifty-miles afar. She had watched and she had tried, too many times to count, to open her daughter's eyes to reality. The reality of her failing relationship. But Jane had accepted the love that she thought she deserved. Love that had dwindled as anorexia regained a tighter hold. Soon enough, Jane felt she was worthy of nothing, so she settled for exactly that.

Mum had warned her, had told her, to spend a little more time in St Andrews with Ophelia and Ada, but Jane hadn't listened, because she refused to believe that her relationship was anything other than "Endgame". She had built her life – her entire university experience – around Zak. She could not afford to lose him, because then she would be left with nothing. She had no real friends in St Andrews, because she had not gone out or socialised or studied in St Andrews. She had always driven to Dundee. And Zak? Zak never came to visit her, because it was "too far". Thirteen miles was too far.

He had had many excuses.
'I'm busy.'
'I'm behind on my diss.'
'Rugby social.'
'Course drinks.'
'Pub quiz.'
'I saw you last weekend.'
'I'm too hungover.'
Always something to do or someone to see.

Following one particularly bad argument, he had confessed that he believed he hadn't got into medical school because of the time he had felt he had had to spend with Jane after she was discharged from the hospital.

He told her that the walks they would have at break times had taken up time he should have spent revising and, with that enlightenment, Jane had felt she couldn't ask him to visit anymore, because he would resent her too much. Her fear of resentment made her desperate and it consumed her.

It changed happy-go-lucky Jane into solemn-and-jealous Jane; jealous of the time he would always manage to find when it came to his course friends or his rugby friends. One particular female friend started to come up more and more frequently, Ali. He would go to watch her dance recitals and became academically "married" to her – things which had never bothered Jane before, but then Jane found her on Facebook. She looked at pictures and thought that Ali was skinner than her. She thought that that was why Zak didn't want to spend time with her anymore because she wasn't as skinny as Ali. She thought that, perhaps, if she lost some weight again, if she got a six-pack like Zak and managed to get rid of her "paunch", then he would pay her a little more attention. He might even ask her to be his girlfriend again. It was the "Toby-effect" making a come-back from Winter 2012. Except this time, Jane had been in a relationship with the boy for three years. Aesthetics should no longer have been a concern.

Jane did not just lose weight, she lost herself. In seeking to control something, anything, she lost it. It was a gap anorexia filled, once again.

She couldn't make Zak spend time with her. She couldn't make him feel something he no longer felt. She desperately clung on to something which was no longer there. She wanted to feel more attractive, she wanted to make him love her more. If Ali was skinny, she needed to be too. What she failed to see was that she was already on the border of an unhealthy weight for her height and with anorexia's return had come the restrictions and the excessive exercise and the blackness.

An Extract from Jane's Diary
March 2017

I wanted to spend my whole life with you, you know.
Still do
But now it's just you.
You're not ready
You're busy
You have a life
Friends

And what do I have ?
An aching heart
A body starved of love for so long it's begun to consume itself.

Because, dear friend
What you fail to realise
Is
That when a person like me
Gives their everything
To a person like you
Who has everything
Then they become a shadow
A collection of sore joints and exposed bones
They find friendship in the voice inside of their head
The promise of a better life
An acceptance
If only I could shed a few pounds
And that's when good old Anna makes her way back into my mind
Proffers her bony hand

But it's ok
Because this time
you can stay away
hide from it
refuse to acknowledge it

I can't.

Zak was her first love. He had been there since the very beginning. She
didn't know what life was like without him and, though the signs were
everywhere, she could not bear to let him go.

So, she starved herself.

She had driven for an hour and a half every day so that she could use a
gym that wasn't in St Andrews - she was too ashamed for anyone there to
see her body. She had failed her Third Year coursework, because her brain
lost its ability to focus and she had started going back to Yorkshire every
weekend. She had realised that she had no one because her someone
was her only one and suddenly, he was becoming a person she no longer

knew. He was cold and indignant. Her messages would go unread for days and her phone calls would be swiftly ended with a 'Sorry can't talk right now' automated text.

Extract from Jane's Diary
March 2017

Instead of telling me you can't cope with me
You hide.
You distance.

I tell myself to take a step back and to relax,
'Stop being so needy or else he'll resent you'

Well, you know what?
I resent you.

When you needed a person, I was that shoulder.
When you needed a mind, I was your sounding board.

But when I needed a heart, yours was absent.
When I shared my words with you, you laughed in response.

Jesus, I was so naïve thinking this time was any different.

I'm not stupid you know.
I've heard how the heart can change
Its mind
Like the head.
I just never thought that it would happen to us. To you.

My heart was always loyal and that's my curse, I guess.
I feel too hard
Love too hard
I commit when commitment isn't reciprocated
I devote when devotion isn't needed.
I starve, when all I hungered for was that feeling – that wholeness
That comes
From being
Loved.

Jane lost herself.

She sacrificed all of the quirks that made her Jane and she forgot what normality looked like. She had thought skinny would make him love her but it just drove him further and further away until, one day – the day outside the gym - she snapped. There was nothing she could do anymore.

This was anorexia, but anorexia now had an accomplice and that accomplice was depression.

* * *

When Jane called Mum from the gym, she had never felt so aggressively alone.

Wilting at her steering wheel, Jane was too exhausted to unbuckle her seatbelt and open the door to go inside and start her workout. She had called Mum, because, subconsciously, she had accepted that she needed help. This was different to last time. Jane was scared because she had been here before. She knew that the control she exercised was not, in reality, control at all. It was a catastrophic loss of it.

Four years on, the manic seventeen-year-old jogging naked on the spot in her Grandma's loft had been replaced by a twenty-year-old student, counting her abs in the basement of a gym. Just as she counted the grapes she ate and the number of branflakes in her bowl, her fingers traced her ribs and hip bones in the same obsessive manner. Instead of wanting to be skinny so that she might be like the other popular girls in Sixth Form, Jane had lost weight in a desperate attempt to feel loved, to be something worthy of love, to fit an image of "attractive" that did not exist in order to make a boy love her. The only similarity was that, once again, it was killing her.

Mum had had to leave her classroom to pick up the call.

She knew that Jane was struggling but there was nothing she could do from two-hundred-and-fifty miles away. She sat and she listened and when Jane said 'I need help' she told her that it was time to come home.

And Jane did.

**An Extract from an email from Jane to Mum
– "Thoughts"**
5th March 2017

Ok, so I have moments where I can see what I'm doing to
myself and like yesterday when I spoke to Zak and after
that I was really motivated to make key changes, hence the
chicken and brown rice soup and the kale chips and the
uncounted fruit and nut butter and honey and chocolate
sauce. But then it's like I wake up into this moment of lucid
consciousness and I regret all the extras I've had and I
feel like I should have counted them and that I need to
take them off my intake for the next day and I feel guilty
and disgusting and fat and then the cycle starts. The cycle
goes in many different directions, it can go from feeling
guilty for not counting, then starting to worry about all the
extra sugar in the fruit and veg that I haven't counted then
thinking about all the super skinny toned girls and models
who are skinnier than me and more toned and who don't
have to eat more and don't have to worry and who do
count fruit and veg and who aren't fat and then I start to
think well why do I have to worry when they are perfectly
fine, then I start to think how my weight isn't even that low
compared to what it was when I was really sick and then
I start to think how I'm just worrying about nothing and
that I'm not really that skinny and how you've said you're
worried about me in the past - like in France ! - and now
looking back I was actually really chubby then so I start to
think can I really trust your judgement or are you always
going to say I'm skinny or you're worried when in reality I
really wasn't skinny at all in France - I was beyond healthy
and probably verging into slightly overweight. I then start
to worry what if I get like that again, what if I listen and I
start not to count fruit and veg and then eating generally
becomes easier and I start getting lazy and not exercising
and not counting and then I start losing my definition
because I don't realise the amount I'm gaining because the
thoughts get weaker and eating becomes more normal and
I just get chubby again. Then there's another cycle where
I start to think about the muscle turning into fat and then
losing my abs and I'm petrified because I've put in a year's

worth of effort to get theses abs and this body and I'm proud and I'm not afraid to show off my arms or tummy because it's tight and I feel defined but then I look at pictures of the summer and my arms are huge and I hate them and I think well if I gain then I'll lose definition and the muscle will go and there will be more fat and I'll need to work out more in order to make the new muscle defined. At the end of the day I'm petrified of that shape I had in France because my face and cheeks are so huge when I smile and my arms are massive and my thighs are huge and toned is so far from what I look like and then I'm scared because I don't want that again and I wasn't beautiful I was so so ugly and I hated myself and I want a nice face with a jaw line and I don't want to be chubby. I just want to be TONED and the way I am now I feel is toned. I'm scared that my fat percentage is going to go up again like it did this week and I'm scared that in gaining I'll lose sight of what I want my body to look like and I'll just get happy with the compromise - the chubby Jane but I won't see it because I'll be living it but everyone else will see how chubby I am and think she's not defined any more, I hated my rolls and my face and everything and the more I think about it the more I hate it and the more scared I am , that makes me want to count fruit and veg and take off the nut butter and all the extras I had yesterday. It makes me terrified of losing definition and becoming ordinary when all I want is the toned body of extraordinary. I don't want to be fat Mum. I want to be beautiful and I don't consider the way I looked in summer beautiful at all. I just see the awful chubbiness in every photo and think how on earth could I have let myself gain that much weight. Then I think I'M NOT EVEN THAT UNDERWEIGHT NOW, why am I even considering all these things like weight gain etc.

I just want to be happy with my body - like I am now to some extent but the shifting in motivation to gain and hatred of gain is SO HARD to live with. It's literally like I'm fighting all the time and I know you'll say it's because you need to gain but do I really? my BMI is basically healthy so do I really need to gain? would you be saying this to someone who doesn't have a history with eating disorders? no! Because you wouldn't be worried because if I always looked like this it would be considered normal. I don't want my muscle to turn to fat, I want to be toned and defined and happy. But at the moment all I can see is hatred of the body I had in France - fear that if I gain I will turn back into that and lose my motivation to stay toned and defined - anxiety and regret at the extra I ate and wanting to take it off today - the reality that I have to count fruit and veg because of the sugar it contains - the fear that you are lying to me like when you said you were worried about me in France and clearly there was no need in hell to be worried about me then.

This is just my attempt to explain what's going on in my head mum. It's like I'm stuck in mud and every time I try and step out it I feel a sensation of ecstatic elevation, the surge to get better and be motivated and see the future I know I can achieve and that I want, but then I fall and I'm pulling so hard to drag myself out of the mud but with my face in the dirt I get hit with this sense of darkness, this shadow which reminds me of all the horrible things that eating will bring, all the things I've worked so hard for which I will lose, the sensation of overly worrying about myself when in reality and in comparison to others and especially other people with eating disorders, I'm fine. The fear of fat percentages and muscle loss and chubbiness and fat - clawing at me and dragging me deeper and deeper into this suffocating and depressing mesh of clotted muddy submersion.

What do I do?

Zak ultimately ended things with Jane over the phone – on her way to a psychiatric assessment. Jane had acknowledged that she had relapsed and had agreed to get help. It was the day before Mother's Day. He called her in the car on the way down to the appointment.

'We're done.'
'What?' Panic.
'That's it. I'm over it.'
'Wait. What are you talking about?'
'Joe saw you and Toby last night. You cheated on me. I'm not doing this anymore Jane. We're done.'
He put the phone down.

Joe had told Zak a lie.
Toby had taken Jane out to try and get her mind off things the night before, but Jane loved Zak and was not the type to cheat. No matter how distant Zak had been.
Jane was sat next to Rosie in the car.

'You ok dude?' Rosie nudged her sister. Jane had turned white.
'He just broke up with me.'
'Oh shit.' Then 'Mum, did you hear that?'
Mum was in deep conversation with Dad and Alex about Alex's birthday presents.
'Mum!'

Mum turned around. 'What Rosie? Don't be so rude! I'm talking!'
'Zak just broke up with Jane.'
'Shit. Simon, turn the radio off. Jane? Jane talk to me. Jane?'
Jane was trying to call Zak back. She was on attempt number eight.
'He's not picking up. Oh my God, Oh my God.'
Jane was crying. Hysterical sort of tears. Tears that were so violent her nose started to bleed.
'Ok, calm down. Calm down!' Mum looked at Rosie. Rosie shrugged – she had no idea what to do but now she was panicking too.
'Simon, pull over.'
Mum was back in control.
'Rosie, try calling him off of your phone.'
Rosie was already dialling.
'Jane, talk to me. What did he say?'
Jane's jumper sleeve was now saturated with blood from her nose. She used her other hand to call Toby. As the dialling tone rang she sobbed, 'he thinks I cheated on him.'
Mum did not even ask 'did you?' She knew her daughter was not capable of it. She saw how deeply in love she was, even if she hated the way Zak treated Jane. Jane did not have it in her. This was a lie but a lie which might, finally, set her daughter free.

* * *

Eventually Jane got through to Toby and explained the misunderstanding. Toby then called Zak who, of course, picked up the phone to his friend. Toby told him the truth – that nothing of the sort had occurred – and Zak eventually called Jane back. He agreed to have a conversation with her in-person the next day. Jane was relieved but not before she had vomited with the stress of the whole miscommunication.

On Mother's Day, Zak met her in the Sainsbury's car park. They walked down to the river. They sat on the bench – their bench - and Zak told Jane that he loved her but he wasn't in love with her.

Jane nodded.
She knew; she just needed him to say it.

She understood that this was the last time that she would say goodbye and that it was over. For good this time. She drove home and she curled up on her bed and for three hours, she wept. At one point, Alex came in and sat beside her. He silently stroked her head. He was seventeen now, the same age as Jane the first time anorexia had come knocking on their front door. He didn't need to say anything; it was all there in his presence. Jane had lost the man that she had thought was her soulmate -the great "love of her life"-but, in his absence, she experienced a different sort of love. A love that came from family and a love that was unspoken, unparalleled and unexpecting.

Jane knew that the hard work she had put in over the last three years was suddenly compromised. She faced the hike towards recovery again, but she knew it would be different this time because she had done it before and she knew that she was capable. She just had to take it at her own pace and remember that she was in control – that this was her future and she was its master.

A couple of days after their conversation, Jane wrote Zak a letter. A letter

Extracts from a letter from Jane to Zak
28th March 2017

Dear Zak

I don't actually know whether I will have the courage to put this note inside your book before returning it to you via some means or other but, even if I don't, writing things down often helps me to process them, so I'll go ahead and address it as if I'm talking to you anyway.

I guess I just want to say that I blame myself for what happened, even though I know I shouldn't. Not because I wasn't loyal to the end - which I was - and not because of me getting poorly again. No. I blame myself for not being able to give you enough even though I gave you my very all. I promised you everything: me, my heart, my loyalty, my mind, my family, my life. I told you I would wait, however long it took. I told you if you needed space, I would stand by and wait until you were ready. I literally gave you all I could possibly physically manage and, emotionally, well, you know how hard I fell for you, and that's what makes dealing with this so hard. We talked about our life together in the future... one which I thought looked so bright, so wonderful and so full of promise, but something changed and I just wasn't enough for you anymore. Truth is, saying goodbye to you this time has split me into pieces and I'm just trying to understand why you thought that walking away was better than committing to me fully, like I have been so devoted to you.

You stole my heart. You pieced me together and you saved me (but this you know because you said it yourself, you thought you could help me) and you most definitely did. You taught me how to love. You made me smile when all I wanted to do was cry. You made me feel loved and want to love so passionately in return at times when I couldn't even bear to be physically touched. You were gentle and kind and everything I could possibly deserve and for that I will be forever grateful. But I fear you stayed because you felt sorry for me – it's what I worry "I thought I could help you "implied. Perhaps it didn't and maybe what started as an act of friendly compassion, sparked a feeling a little more intense. That thing people call love.

20% of my life has had you as its central figure, you as my person, you as my best friend. No wonder letting you go is so hard, but, at the end of the day, you told me you didn't think you were right for me and that I wasn't right for you.

Of all of the things about you that I miss; your eyes, your hands, your face. The way that you would pull me close (especially in the mornings and not let me go). Your stupid chat and how passionate I could tell you were when we talked about medicine or Wilde. I guess hearing that you didn't think we were right for each other is what hurts me the most. Because you made me a better person. You taught me how to feel and how to find happiness in the unhappiest of times.

I just wanted to say that. I wanted you to know that. You literally brought me back to life and for that I will never stop loving you. But I want you to be happy. So gloriously and spectacularly happy.

I also know that I have to stop blaming myself for not being enough - because I loved enough for the both of us for a good two months and it literally broke me. Emotionally I couldn't have given you anymore, physically making the journey to Dundee every week a few times a week in the hope of seeing you whenever you called – well that exhausted me. And I needed you and I know that that might be hard for you to hear and I know that it's awful of me to say, but I'm trying to be completely honest and so I have to say it in order to be true to myself and true to you too.

I needed you, both physically and emotionally, but I told you that your needs came first - your dissertation and degree – and I could see that, so

I made a promise that I would wait. I tried to make it as easy as possible for you so that your life could be as stress-free as possible and so that you could be happy. But, in doing so, in sacrificing so much of my own self-respect, self-worth and dignity - at coming to you whenever you needed me but not telling you when I needed you for fear you would resent me for it – I became a shell of myself and perhaps that's why you chose to say goodbye.

I know that you are capable of great things. You are a unique and wonderful person. You have a heart worthy of so much love and, although I tried to give you enough, I don't know whether I personally was enough for you and it kills me because that's all I ever wanted. You will be an amazing doctor and I know your Mum will be so bloody proud of you when you graduate and so will I.

I suppose I should stop talking now – it's been the best four years of my life. We've had a bumpy road but 80% of my memories are good ones. I want you to be happy and whole and loved and cared for and I'm sure that someone, someday, more worthy than I, someone better and beautiful and brilliant and un-broken. Someone normal. They will find their way to you and give you everything I just couldn't. Good luck and goodbye Mr. It's been a pleasure.

J x

In writing the letter, she had hoped that it would enable her to put his presence behind her, to lay the memories to bed and allow herself to move on with a clear head. However, with the best will in the world, fixing a broken heart requires more than words on a page.

What Jane had to realise, was that the only thing that would soothe her pain was time and time was something she could not control – or at least its passing.

Her pain at losing Zak would be blue for a while, tears and an aching and good memories weighing heavy on her heart. With time, it would glow red with shades of anger, resentment and frustration. Eventually, it would pale into pastel insignificance. Time heals heartbreak, it cannot heal mental illness. The latter requires assertion, an active awareness of the problem and a desire to resolve, three things which Jane had plenty of now, once her attention lost its focus on Zak and returned to remembering who she was. Who Jane was as an entity independent of her relationship.

* * *

The first few months after Jane's relapse saw her twenty-first birthday in April and her parents' twenty-fifth wedding anniversary in June. Pictures taken at this time are not of Jane, but of a skeleton. Though her family tried to make the events as special and "normal" as possible, Jane could not hide the dwindling frame of her body – no matter how hard she tried.

Her twenty-first birthday was meant to end in a night out at the local club. Instead, Jane arrived at the venue and had to be driven home within twenty minutes because she was so drunk that she couldn't stand. She had had two glasses of prosecco and a jelly shot, but she was so underweight that the alcohol went straight to her head. Mum had to take out her contact lenses and sit beside her when they had brought her home. She watched her sleep so that she didn't choke on her own vomit and Rosie spent the evening entertaining all of Jane's old school friends who had come to celebrate with her. It wasn't the most memorable experience, but it proved to Jane that she had a lot of work to do in order to get back to where she needed to be.

The first-time anorexia took a hold on Jane, she didn't believe that she was ill. The second time around, Jane was well aware of what was happening and she elected to do everything she could do fix it.

Her twenty-first birthday was her lowest point. After that, the days started to get clearer and her mind had a focus that wasn't Zak or trying to be something she was not. This time, she had a greater lucidity of thought and her own voice was not drowned out by the malicious and venomous spite anorexia had had a way of forcing her to project in the past.

In 2013, Dad had tended to be the most common victim of Jane's anger, even if he had done nothing wrong. This was why, when it came to her parents' anniversary, Jane saw it as a day of victory over anorexia, rather than one of defeat, because it was the day she allowed Dad back in. The day she forgave him for a loving her too hard.

* * *

Until the age of sixteen, Jane had been her "father's daughter".

They had built boot-boxes and fought over Wii golf. He had watched her play in every single hockey game and taught her how to build walls and patios – they had been inseparable. Jane's eating disorder destroyed their relationship for no reason other than the fact that Dad simply did not understand. Anorexia has a way of obliterating trust, no matter how many years it has been built over. For Jane, it took away the bond she had developed with her father. He had done absolutely nothing wrong, except maybe love his daughter a little too much. His pride in all of his children was something Jane struggled to process for she didn't understand why anyone would be proud of her. She did not feel worthy of "unprecedented" accolade. Jane's illness was not Dad's fault, but the way the eating disorder manifested itself and changed Jane's personality and behaviour, meant that it was Dad who fell victim to anorexia's wrath.

Jane still loved her Dad. She never hated him, nor Rosie, nor Alex. They were her family and they taught her what it was to be a part of something so sacred that even the strain of mental illness could not break that bond. It grew threadbare and tangled but it remained present and, with time, patience and an awful lot more love, it was built back up again. A rope whose sturdy knots were indestructible.

In the years following 2013, after the hardest battle was over, Jane faced another – rebuilding the bridges between her and her father and her and her younger brother. Though they never stopped loving her nor she them, something shifted in the dynamic which had existed before and Jane knew that it would not be as easy as discharge from CAMHS and an immediate return to being "Daddy's girl".

The day eventually came, that summer – summer 2017 - three years later, at her parents' anniversary party. A song came on that Dad had played to them, when they were younger, on the CD player in the car on long drives or in the kitchen on Sunday mornings. Every time he would turn to them -glance over his shoulder if he was driving – and say to Rosie and Jane and Mum, 'this song is about my girls'. When the song came on in the little village hall that sunny afternoon, Jane ran outside to find Dad and made him dance with her. In that moment, Jane knew that the fissure between them was finally healed – even if she was battling the demons that had broken it in the first place so fortuitously, once again. The love she felt overwhelmed her and, when the song was over and he had given her a squeeze before running off to help with the Hog Roast, she took herself to the bathroom for a moment. She allowed the swelling in her chest to settle, wiped happy tears from her eyes and took a deep breath. Jane was now a "Mummy's girl", but she was also, finally, back to being her father's daughter. It had taken four years, but it was worth it.

* * *

The summer of 2017 was spent healing. Jane focused on herself and on her recovery. She was nervous for her final year as an undergraduate, because she did not know what being a student truly entailed. She had been 'Zak's Girlfriend' for the entirety of her time at St Andrews and now she was Jane. Jane with her own identity. Jane who was independent and Jane who was excited to experience (finally) life as a single, twenty-one-year-old, St Andrean student.

Jane could not have known that the experiences ahead of her in the next nine months would make her feel so alive - so brilliantly human - that she would end up staying for another three years. The first three years in St Andrews had been dictated by her relationship and all of its ups and downs. The next four would be about Jane. St Andrews was her town. It was full of friends and faces that would become her people.
She knew that she had already wasted too much time, she couldn't afford to waste a minute more.

Chapter 11
St Andrews

Nineteen, sixty-eight, fourteen and, finally, number one.

Over the next four years, Jane made her way across St Andrews and each and every house brought with it its own learning curves, self-actualisation and memories.

In every flat, she found herself sharing with someone who had suffered from (or was still struggling with) an eating disorder. Every time she realised that they shared a demon she felt as if the universe was testing her. She could not seem to escape girls like her. Though her experiences with them gave her a greater understanding of what it was like to live with eating disorders other than anorexia (bulimia in particular) in a domestic setting, she did not let their behaviours trigger her. Jane knew that recovery was not simple and she wanted to support the girls she met who were struggling, rather than seeing them as competition or something to aspire to.

An Extract from Jane's Diary
September 2017

Sometimes I think that having had this illness, I've developed a sixth sense to my fellow strugglers. It's like I attract them or something. A mating-call I guess? I can look at a person and know, instantly, that something isn't quite right. It doesn't have to be because they are super skinny – I'm not anymore – it can be the way they dress in oversized clothes or their choice of coffee. Sometimes it's the way they eat their food, not even what they order – I see it a lot when I'm in the café. It breaks my heart, truly. There are so many people here in this town that struggle the same way I used to. I know I'm not out of the woods just yet, but when I see girls that have thighs so slim you could break them - instead of making me want to run to the gym and spin on the bike till I can't walk anymore - it makes me want to cry.

They aren't living. I just wish I could shake them. Shake them till all the bad is out and they have room to let the good in. It's so hard but I know that if it were me, when I was at my lowest, I wouldn't have believed a word they said. Body dysmorphia is the worst part — everyone else can see but you.

2017 to 2018 was the year of chaos.

2018 to 2019 was the year of chastity.

2019 to 2020 was the year of change.

Each year brought with it ups and downs in weight, struggles with body image and struggles with self-worth. Challenges called for solutions and Jane developed a vast array of coping mechanisms which, though at times unhealthy, eventually settled her into a routine which she came to call her own "normal".

The year of chaos.
When Jane arrived at the little red door of number nineteen in September 2017, she was excited. For the first time in three years, she was going to university as a single woman and, though she had neglected her friendships in St Andrews for the entirety of that time, she was ready to invest every moment she had left in fixing the fractures formed as a result. She was hungry to meet new people and anxious to make new memories.

Jane spent the first semester experimenting with "Tinder" and writing her dissertation, 'Self-Induced Starvation or Survival: Representations of Teenage Eating Disorders in Contemporary Women's Writing'. Both were significant achievements. The former, an experiment in self-promotion and self-confidence. The latter, a self-reflective and educational piece of work, which saw Jane learn about other female writers and their own experiences with anorexia and bulimia. She admired how they refrained from glorifying or detailing the accounts of their own struggles in their writing — something which could have been deemed triggering, had they stylised their narratives in different ways. The works she examined were creative adaptions, tales which told stories that were either rooted in the fantastical and mythological or adopted a form of poetry that celebrated the sheer power of the female body. Her research made her feel empowered and, slowly but surely, she began to step away from her strict (and rather monotonous) routine:

1.   Wake up
2.   Ab Workout
3.   Breakfast
4.   Gym
5.   Study
6.   Shift
7.   Dinner
8.   Bed + Netflix

Instead of eating the same menu of tasteless food every day, she started to host weekly themed dinners: Thai, Indian, Mexican, Lebanese, Italian. Eating with people was a challenge and Jane wanted to test herself. She ate food that wasn't strictly calorie controlled because the company and the laughter and the happiness that eating with friends fostered filled her in a new type of way. It felt so much more rewarding. She didn't feel guilt when it came to sharing food with friends because they ate together – she could rationalise it because everyone was partaking in the same action – it was not just her. She embraced the unity she found through food and saw it as a celebration of being alive and being normal - something that a lonely bowl of porridge in bed just didn't quite match.

As she began to eat more freely, her confidence in other aspects of her life started to strengthen and she decided that it was worth investing a little money in the university's plethora of social events.

St Andrews is renowned for hosting many, many, Balls. The first of the year was Opening Ball – Jane had missed this one. The next one to come up was the annual Welly Ball. Held in Kinkell Byre, Welly Ball is a popular favourite amidst St Andrews students, mainly because the shoe wear protocol is explicitly "no-heels-allowed".   Up until the Welly Ball of October 2017, Jane had been to two balls in three years: Opening Ball in her First Year and her student accommodation Ball in Third Year. She hadn't known much about the others because, whenever they had occurred, she had tended to be socialising in Dundee. This year, however, on a cold Saturday night, she found herself a little tipsy in a short black dress, cropped black jacket and a pair of borrowed black Hunter wellies. When she arrived, she looked around her and saw more fellow students than she had ever before. Students that weren't sat in lecture theatres or queuing for a space in the library. Students dressed up to the nines in tuxedos and ball gowns. Students being students in the most St Andrews way they knew how. It was while standing in the queue for the toilet, smiling through shivers as a random girl in the line behind her took a photo, that she finally felt a part of something, her first real taste of the university culture she had been blind to. From that moment, the moment in the queue, she became addicted to belonging to a way of living that she had ostracised herself from, albeit un-purposefully. She wanted to make her time there count and the Welly Ball of 2017 cemented her desire to stay just as socially involved as she was intellectually.

Jane had always wondered what it was like to work behind the bar at the Students' Union.
She had worked at the coffee shop there for nearly three years and loved it, but bartending appealed to her more reckless side, a job that involved popular music and late nights rather than classical radio and early mornings. Up until that year, she had been too scared to apply but, with a new mindset and renewed sense of confidence, she decided to just go for it.

One week (and an email of inquiry to the bar manager) later, she found herself dressed in a Coors Light t-shirt, nervously walking up the hill from number nineteen for her first ever shift. A shift which turned out to be one of the best nights of Jane's life and instigated a permanent career shift - barista to bartender - introducing her to a family of students that served to further her understanding of what it was to belong.

Jane could count on one hand the number of times she had been drinking at the Students' Union by the time November 2017 came around. She always tended to get too drunk at the pre-drinks and never ended up making it out to the bars.

Within the space of two months, she had made up for three years of wasted time.

On her first shift she was placed on a till with two second year boys, Robbie and Seb. They were cheeky, gregarious and two of the most charismatic people she had ever met. They immediately engaged with her in conversation and told her that they had seen her, many times, at the gym but she always seemed so "in the zone" that they were too afraid to come over and disturb her. She knew who they were because, just as they had seen her, she had spied them. One of them was blond and had a jawline that looked as if it had been carved out of stone. His eyes were the sort of blue that penetrated the soul. He was confident, handsome and knew his eyes had a transfixing sort of power. That was Seb. Robbie was a little less cocky, but just as loud and energetic. He was American and very dark in his features – more polite than Seb but equally as fun to be around.

At the end of the shift, she offered them a ride home – they lived a good two miles out of town and it was approaching 3am. Grateful was an understatement. Before they could leave, they told her that they had to find their friend, Felix, who also worked at the bar, but had been out drinking that night rather than working. Once Felix had been found and the trio was complete, they all piled into Jane's car, stopping only twice so that Felix could vomit partially digested remnants of tuna pasta out of the door. It was a bonding experience quite like no other.

Seb and Robbie had made Jane's first shift fly by. In welcoming her with such openness into their bar staff family (and also their friendship circle), Jane knew that she was about to become a part of something special. Good things were to come.

The boys introduced her to their friends, all Second Year students and all people who she felt instantly connected to. Jane felt as if she was meant to belong to the class of 2020, despite being due to graduate in 2018. When she was around them, she no longer felt like a nobody. They taught her how to drink and she taught them how to bake. She discovered the reality of a real night out – that it went from pre-drinks to 'Union' to Afterparty to the Take-Away and (occasionally) to One-Night-Stand – and that you were allowed to drink on Sundays and Mondays, just as you were the weekends.

An Extract from Jane's Diary
April 2018

Lost in alcohol induced stupor, I danced in the haze of poor decision and recklessness. I met boys that acted like boys; they weren't pretending to be something that they weren't. They were honest in their immaturity and they taught me what university living was meant to look like.

I learnt that sex and love are two very different things. My old-fashioned belief that they were synonymous was dissolved and, I suppose, I experienced an awakening of sorts.

Sex was something that was meant to be fun. It was meant to be spontaneous and impulsive. It was about two people, not just one. Two people that wanted to feel good and wanted to make one another feel good and that? That was exciting and empowering and very, very different. It was almost addictive.

I realised that I didn't have to diet and restrict my food intake in the hours prior to engaging in the act like I had with Zak. Though he had never commented on my weight, I always feared he would think my bloating was fat. I also always knew when it was going to happen with him. In our relationship, there wasn't spontaneity, more a sort of unspoken expectation. One I definitely didn't object to, but one that always led to overthinking – before, during and after.

In this new life I was living, most of the time sex happened, I hadn't known it was going to. That was the beauty of it. Usually, I had eaten freely during the daytime and drunk excessively in the evening. I hadn't planned to go home with anyone – never did, actually - but then I would find myself hitting it off, chatting or sharing a cig, and all of a sudden, we were walking back to his or mine Sometimes he was just walking me home, sometimes I just felt like inviting him inside. I wasn't promiscuous, but I was a lot more confident and I think that they found that attractive.

For so long I had felt ugly. I had been ashamed of my body. I didn't want anyone to see it because I thought they would be repulsed by it too. My dysmorphia was crippling but as I drank more, the inhibitions faded away and the calories didn't seem to count anymore. These people liked me for me, not for my bones, but for my curves. They hadn't met "skinny Jane", they only knew" healthy Jane". My own insecurities were unexpectedly buried - the soft soil of insobriety - and, with alcohol as my new best friend, I stopped caring about the numbers. Number of calories, number of workouts and the number on the scale. It was far from healthy, but it was new and the newness was magnetic. I became obsessed with testing my new-found self-awareness and, instead of spending every night alone miserably self-scolding as I scrolled through the list of food I'd eaten that day on my phone, I broke the cycle of militant control - I stopped giving a fuck.

Jane threw herself into absolutely everything.

Every night she wasn't working at the bar she was drinking. Though she thought her time in "The Bubble" was limited, it didn't matter because she had found her people and they were adamant on making the most of every opportunity. Jane went to Polo and to May Ball. She went to brunches and drank mimosas. She walked along the beach and drank instant coffee perched on porches. She started smoking. Robbie began training her at the gym and Felix educated her with music. Seb continued to charm her with his azure stare and, though theirs was a rather topsy-turvy friendship at times, he seemed to understand her and her psychological turmoil in a way that no-one had ever really been able to before.

Her change in lifestyle was not one that came without consequences and, unfortunately, they were largely physical in their manifestation. With more time spent on her feet (working or dancing), the hip issues which had emerged as a result of her anorexia made a return and she had to stop doing cardio exercise at the gym. Less cardio exercise and a continued "party lifestyle" meant that she gained weight - around two stone in two months - but she was so preoccupied with living in each and every moment, rather than thinking about every decision that she made, that it wasn't until she drove back home to spend the summer with her family, that the reality of her new lifestyle choices hit her.

It was horrifying and she was mortified.

Jane found that the person who stared back at her in the bathroom mirror wasn't the girl that had left for Scotland a year earlier. Though her face was rounded and rosy with the healthy blush of memories well-made, the curves she had developed in places that had previously been a landscape of bone-built mountains were not so comfortably received. No longer sharp and bruised, the summits had softened into hills topped with flesh rather than taut skin. It was a new terrain, an unfamiliar one, one of mature femininity and one which no longer required the thermal down of Laguna hair in order to protect its troubled ground.

In freeing herself from a preoccupation with being invisible and in living a life that was her own, rather than one determined by the voice inside her head - it was a woman that looked back at Jane, not a troubled and starving child. But she, too, was also damaged.

On closer inspection, blemishes were breaking through her skin – the toxins from the alcohol making their presence known. They reminded Jane of her impulsive choices – things she later came to consider mistakes. The roundness of her cheeks was, to her, a sign of weakness – an inability to exercise self-restraint. She was to be punished for her gluttony through entrapment in a body which she despised. A body whose reflection she now had to look at every day.

An Extract from Jane's Diary
June 2018

I had to drag myself out of the black depression of guilt, veined with self-hatred, for the third time. But this was worse than ever before because I had become the very version of myself I feared the most.

The "Fat" one.

It took her the entire summer and a solo adventure around America, Canada and Italy, but when Jane landed in Edinburgh in September, she was tanned, a little lighter than she had been the last time she was in Scotland and excited for a life post-degree. She had planned to couch-surf for a week in St Andrews whilst working a final 'Freshers'' at the bar. She would make some quick money which she could use for a deposit on a flat and then she would commence the search for a full-time job – perhaps as a chef or teacher.

All these 'could's' and 'would's' had solid foundations – plans enabling Jane to move on with her life – but the world works in funny ways and, it just so happened, that Jane would not actually be leaving St Andrews for another three years.

The Scottish seaside town was not ready for her to leave just yet.

The year of chastity.
Freshers' week came and went and Jane remembered how addicted she was to the feeling of being known. She had established herself in some big circles in the last year - many of them were with people who were only halfway through their degrees. When she walked down the street to the 'Union' , she would see people she knew – people that would smile and come over for a hug and a quick chat. Never in the three years prior to her break-up with Zak had she walked down the street and been stopped by a friend. Now, it took her twenty minutes, rather than two, to get from one end of Market Street to the other.
The combination of feeling wanted and feeling as if she actually belonged

meant that she began considering what it would be like if she found a job in St Andrews to keep her busy, rather than back home. She had friends in St Andrews and another job already at the bar if she wanted to work two jobs at once. Most importantly though, she felt safe. The "year of chaos" had seen Jane construct the scaffolding of something rather extraordinary in Scotland. There was a framework there, ready to be filled, and she warmed to the idea of finishing her masterpiece.

And so, the building began.

She found a job at a little café on the main street and she fell in love with the locals just as quickly as she had the students. She made coffee and baked cakes and spent her mornings nattering on to Steve about his five different cars or listening to Charlotte complain about the scones being too big. She met a soul-sister in her manager, Annie, and they would spend Monday mornings giggling with sleepy smiles whilst eating gluten-free crumpets. Annie made work not seem like work and every time Jane walked through the big glass door, she was overcome with a sense of calm. This was her place and these were her people.

An Extract from Jane's Diary
December 2018

I've fallen in love with the people that make this town. The locals, the students and the incredible souls I work with at the café. My 'Dell' family have taught me perspective. That life is life, work is work and at the end of the day, whatever chaos unravels, we are in it together and as a team. They are my oasis when the intensity of life gets a little too much. They love me for who I am, the dyspraxic, dyslexic specky four eyed Jane. When I am sad they are always ready with a peppermint tea and some ridiculous story to make me laugh. When I miss home, I remember that they are my home and a part of me will always be Little Jane from the 'Dell' because the 'Dell' will always have a little piece of Jane.

She found a flat – number sixty-eight. She moved in with two Third Year girls, Sophia and Penelope, and a Second Year one called Jenna. Sophia and Penelope were part of the same circle that Robbie, Seb and Felix had introduced her to. Jane had never lived with American girls before, or any girls for that matter – other than her Fourth Year flatmate who she didn't see all that much. Jane felt like she was experiencing university residence life for the first time, for the house was never empty.

One of the girls in the flat was bulimic and Jane knew after three hours of living in the house. Her last flatmate had had the same eating disorder and, though Jane had never heard her vomiting, the smell in the toilet and mountains of empty diet coke bottles told her all that she needed to know. This flatmate preferred sparkling water and it was the less the smell, more the wads of carefully placed toilet tissue at the bottom of the toilet, that gave her away. Jane gave it a week or so of living in the house before she broached the topic with her. They had a few drinks first. Jane found that eating disorders tended to be the sort of topic people found easier discussing when they had lost their inhibitions - weed and alcohol were particularly good at loosening the tongue. After a frank and bleary-eyed heart to heart, Jane told her flatmate that she was going to help her, because life in recovery was like living in a different world. She promised her that she would do everything she could to support her and that if she saw her struggling she would try her hardest to intervene in the most supportive way possible. Her flatmate thanked her. In acknowledging and confronting the issue by explicitly telling her flatmate that she was aware of her behaviour and tendencies, Jane made sure that there was no way her flatmate could escape the reality of her illness – the secret was now shared. Sometimes mere recognition of an issue, one that has gone unnoticed or been kept secret for so long, is enough to break the spiral of toxic behavioural deceit. The shame becomes an open one and the secret becomes manifested as something real, not purely imagined.

Though her relationship with this particular flatmate was sometimes strained, Jane tried to help her whenever she could. She did, however, have to keep a certain distance for selfish reasons. She could not afford to relapse again, especially with bulimic tendencies rather than anorexic. She was aware of the attraction, the promise of a self-control that superseded any other, but she also knew that if she fell into it, in actuality, the very opposite would occur; loss of control. A flirtation with disordered eating was not something Jane could do, for it always led to development of a toxic relationship. Knowing enough about herself to limit her interactions with her flatmate was a sign that Jane was becoming more self-aware, especially when it came to her own trigger-points and catalysts.

Penelope was a football girl and with her sport came her teammates. Sixty-eight was their haven - when they weren't in the library or on the pitch - and Jane loved it. They would invite her to their Wednesday night socials and, though she was almost always working, seeing their flushed faces pop up in front of her at the bar would make her night. Penelope was blonde and bubbly and the very definition of New Hampshire. She made Jane laugh from her belly. Their sex lives (or lack thereof) were just as pathetic as each other's and they bonded over their bleak chaste situations with mugs of Nespresso and peanut butter spooned into their mouths straight out of the jar.

Jane's relationship with Sophia was a little more serious. Sophia was sensitive and could tell when Jane was upset or something wasn't quite right. Where Penelope was just as self-sabotaging as Jane in her choice of men, Sophia would be the voice of reason. She saw the good ones and made it clear when she thought a bad one was about. She advised Jane with logic and emotional intelligence and their conversations always felt like they cured the soul. At least for a while. Sophia's twenty-first birthday party in December was the first informal "formal dinner" Jane had been invited to in five years and, as a significant proportion of the student body in St Andrews were American, the culture of twenty-first birthday celebrations was a well-established and hugely popular one.

That night, they had all got ready together and walked down to the venue with Sophia's parents. Robbie, Felix and Seb were there, as were their friends and all of the football girls that Jane had grown to call sisters. That night became one of Jane's most treasured in St Andrews. As she sat at the table and looked around her, she finally thought that, yes, here was where she was meant to be. She ate and she drank and she stumbled home and vomited all over her bed, but it was a night like no other and, in inviting her to be a part of it, Sophia had made Jane feel so much more than special; she had made her feel wanted.

The three months Jane had spent with Sophia, Penelope and Jenna in the run up to Christmas had made her think. She had been considering the creative writing programme at St Andrews and, having unsuccessfully applied for the poetry one at the end of 2018, she decided to give it one last shot and apply again, this time for prose. Jane wanted to stay, she had always felt like she was meant to be a 2020 graduate and she knew that words were the way she felt best able to convey her thoughts, feelings and emotions. It made sense.

For the entirety of January, Jane was alone in sixty-eight and she began her application. There were very few hours going at the café and the bar was closed until the students came back and so, Jane wrote.

An Extract from Jane's Diary
January 2019

My happy is Words.

Words that sound like something they aren't. Words that mean something they sound like they don't. Words that tail off into tapered meaninglessness. Words that end conversations as bluntly as they begin them. Words that are empty sounds and signs until they scrabble together into chains of prose. Beautiful prose. Words that make people cry and laugh and hate and love. Words that find their power in the phrases that they jigsaw. Words that mean nothing until they are spoken aloud. Words with rhythm. Words without. Words that aren't words, well, "real" words.

I say these words and I write these words and I think these words.

I sing these words in the shower and I dream these words in my sleep.

I do not know why these words are the words that choose to form themselves on a tired tongue. Words that reverberate in the cavern of my mouth, from the back of my throat to the space between my company and I. Me and my shower head. Me and my pillowcase.
But they do.

These words are impulsive.

They spurt out in an accent which changes as swiftly as my thoughts. They speckle pages with black marks accompanied with the tiptaptiptaptiptapping of a keyboard tango. A tempo ebbing and flowing in perfect nonsensical harmony to the mumblings of my busy head.

Throughout all of this time, Jane had been focusing on herself. She hadn't been intimate with anyone since October and wouldn't till the following October – a year to the day. Though she had initially missed physical intimacy, the longer she went without it, the more she grew to fear it. As time went on, the fear grew stronger and she stopped searching. Her nights out no longer ended in recklessness, they were usually spent stumbling around her kitchen making 'drunk food'. She deleted dating apps – she no longer had the confidence to meet the match behind her phone screen. She distanced herself from men she had had feelings for in the past and started to regularly deactivate her social media pages so that she would not be bombarded with post after post of happy couples and people "in love". She had her jobs, her flatmates and her social life. She didn't need a boyfriend or a regular hook-up because she was perfectly happy alone. It took her many months to realise it, because, for a very long time, she had thought she needed someone else to make her feel valid or provide her with affirmation and support. However, in her chastity, she realised she was independent and she thrived off it. She could run at her own pace with her own schedule, do what she wanted when she wanted and wasn't restricted to certain plans or another person's routine. She could flirt without fear of causing offence and though, at times, she occasionally found her eyes wandering towards people she could have had the same sort of fun with that she had back in 2015, she taught herself self-restraint and she felt the better for it.

With the return of Spring, she went to Polo (again), attended the fashion shows and drank more mimosas and instant coffee perched in porches. She attended many more twenty-first birthday celebrations and went to May Ball in a black dress that made her feel like a princess. She was in the middle of a quiet afternoon shift at the café one Wednesday in late May when the email came through confirming her offer of a place on the MLitt. course. She cried and so did Annie and that night she celebrated with gin and ginger beer. When Jane left number sixty-eight that summer, it wasn't with a heavy heart, for she knew come September she would be back, one last time, and that she would finally have a purpose. She hoped that this focus, the M.Litt., would enable her to finish her time in the St Andrews "bubble" with a sense of fulfilment and completion. This time would be the last time, no more loose strings and unsaid goodbyes.

The year of change.
Jane purchased an old convertible the week prior to driving back up to Scotland for her final year. She called her Lola and the lock on the driver's door was very temperamental so she had to climb out of the passenger door every time she stopped driving. Lola was a character, just like her owner, but despite her faults, she provided Jane with a sensation of release – driving without a roof - and this gave her the ability to calm her anxiety in a way she had never really been capable of doing.

Miller's Road was a beautiful place. The house Jane lived in looked like it had been pulled right out of a "Country Home" magazine and every time she walked up the drive, she couldn't help but feel lucky. Lucky to call it "home". She started her time there in the biggest room but, after a couple of months of waking up and being so cold that she could see her breath, she moved into the smallest room at the front of the house. It had a big bay window which looked out onto the front lawn and paper-thin blinds which meant Jane couldn't help but be woken at sunrise every morning. It was a gentle alarm, kind in its nudge to wake her. Miller's Road was a stone's throw away from the beach and, when the days tended to be a little harder, Jane would often walk down to the Old Course to watch the sky run red and yellow as the sun set. Daniel occupied the room next door and he was like a younger brother to her. She had met him the previous year when she had been "adopted" (as per St Andrews tradition) into an academic family, despite not actually being a student at the time, and they had forged a friendship bordering on fraternal. Jane had two other flatmates, in one of whom she found a soul sister. Her name was Ailia.

Ailia had struggled with the same issues as Jane had in the past, but, just like Jane, she had fallen in love with the light of a life absent of anorexia and was doing everything she could to make up for lost time. This was Jane's first experience of living with a fellow songbird who was at the same point in her recovery – it was wonderful. Though Ailia was rarely in the house, as she would stay at her boyfriend's whenever she could, when she was around, they would sit huddled next to a space heater and talk about all the reasons why recovery was worth it. Ailia told Jane that she should love her body and all of its lumps and bumps and curvy loveliness because they were shapes formed out of love. Love for cheese and love for chutney. Love for chocolate covered brazil nuts and Honey Jack Daniels. Love for food shared with friends at potlucks and picnics. Love for a body that had been through the mill, but that had emerged, despite its abuse, bold and beautiful and brave.
Ailia was a breath of fresh air.

Between September and December, Jane worked herself into the ground at the café and the bar and at the gym. Though anorexia was no longer a prevalent demon, her anxiety and depression were finding ways to resurface and, in a desperate attempt to drown them out, she preoccupied herself with as many distractions as she possibly could. She started seeing a boy after not having had a boyfriend for nearly three years and, though they were only together for a month, he showed Jane that she was someone who could be loved and someone who deserved it. Jane couldn't process or accept this. She did not feel worthy of the pedestal she thought he put her on – albeit accidentally. They broke up and she found preoccupation in forgetting herself. Once again, into the spiral of self-sabotage she span.

She started drinking again – a lot – and with the drink came the smoking
and the inhibition-less 'drunk food', two things which had been major
contributors to her weight gain in 2018. She found moments of happiness in
the distractions of friends, parties and classes but they were transitory and
fleeting and they never made her feel truly whole. They were moments that
dissolved into time just as quickly as they emerged and, in failing to address
her issues, they began to overwhelm her.

An Extract from Jane's Diary
December 2019

I am impulsive.

For my happy is brief.
It is stolen from sunsets and secret chocolate buttons. It is taken from the
smiles of people I love and is woven into my peripheral thoughts till I find
myself alone. Again.

It is the magic of alcohol's inhibition-removing power. It is driving in the
dark with the roof down and clean air blowing everything not present in
that singular transitory moment
away.
It is the beach. It is the sound of the sea and the smell of the sand and the
way that the sky bleeds red.

Clouds sitting upon horizons pregnant with snow.

It is dissolving into a warm embrace when my heart hurts and my head
aches with dehydrated sadness. It is the heat of the tumble dryer and
the aroma of clean laundry. It is hiding my face in sheets still wrapped
in residual warmth from the spinning drum of the machine. Happiness
grounded in touch and smell and sight and taste. Happiness that lasts just
about as long as it takes for the kettle to boil or corn to pop.

But then it all goes black again and I'm left feeling utterly broken and
alone.

The Little Red Balloon was faltering, but this time, it wasn't a rock bottom
where food was the foundation, instead, it was sadness.

Chapter 12
Guilt

An Extract from Jane's Diary
February 2020

I have been sad for a what feels like a very long time.

I occupied every moment of my days with a constant preoccupation with
people.
The desire to be needed has caused me to pursue, with an almost obsessive
intensity, a need for purpose. My mind has been in constant chaos, from
the moment I blink open sleepy eyes in the morning, to the second I close
them at night. My dreams have been absent of colour and, memorably,
unmemorable. Exhaustion has clouded my conscious thoughts, starved my
brain of the ability to rationalise and left it trudging through the vanguard
of a lonely routine painted in the façade of fake friendships and weary
smiles. I have desperately battled to stay afloat in a sea of self-hatred and
self-deprecation. For years now, I have somehow, miraculously, managed
to survive on gasped breaths of the air of "stability", but this has only left
me breathless, for my anxious inhalation has been temporary.

Friends I thought were friends were, in fact, ships that passed me in my very
own black night, their silhouettes shifting through my mind, in and out of my
days. I only recently came to realise that the "light" of their presence was
but a temporary glow, the glimmer of false promises which was, in reality,
no foundation for true friendship at all. My life was a constant torrent of
people.
Faces I met at work or at the gym, people I would structure my days around
and people who would never scaffold me into theirs. People who took
from me what they needed, when they needed, without the conscience or
empathy I nurtured for them. People that couldn't have cared less whether
I emerged from the darkness or whether, instead, I dwelled in its depths for

what felt like an eternity.

These people I thought were more than just people gave me a false understanding of what it was to be living. They made me realise the importance of honesty - of being a genuine person - but not through lessons learnt in awe of them. Instead, I experienced this harsh epiphany purely in response to the disappointment and heartbreak they left in their desertion.

Trust is something that builds over time. I was too trusting in those I had only just met, because I underestimated the significance of what trust meant for other people. There are many things a person can do to break your trust; sharing a secret that wasn't meant to be spoken, proffering your views and opinions as their own, stabbing knives into your back when you least expect it – all things that would not happen if you truly got to know a person before you opened up your heart to them. I think, for a while, I mistook honesty for trust. The two are not, of course, mutually exclusive, but honesty is a trait I value above all else. If a person told me a truth, I believed that it automatically made them genuine.

The truth about who I was, who I wanted to be, was a foreign a concept. In my struggle to know this person, the I , the me, the soul who occupied my brain and body, I became desperately dependent on finding this truth through other peoples' eyes. I used their response, the value they placed on me, to act as my foothold to who this person was.
To determine what was real and what was make-believe.
I suppose that a part of me wanted to see if other people could see in me what I so greatly sought– the essence of who I was – and that this would enable me to figure out what made me me. However, life does not work like that.

Instead of finding the clarity I craved, I found myself spiralling deeper and deeper into the abyss of my very own unknown until, one day, it all got a little too much.

I have done many things in my life I am not proud of.

I have made decisions, which, though more often than not, were drunken misjudgements or impulse acts made at the height of depression's low, I regret. I let these mistakes puddle in my brain and dampen any true feelings of happiness which spontaneously arose. They steeped my self-esteem in a tirade of shame and though, on reflection, I know that these were small errors in judgement that are all part and parcel of being human, I allowed them to define me. In doing so, I lost the true spirit of who I was.

The way I feel "Guilt" can be paralysing.

Guilt for being a bad daughter, guilt for being a bad sister, guilt for being a bad friend and guilt for being a bad person. Guilt every time I didn't work-out for long enough - despite running on four hours sleep and juggling two jobs – and guilt for every single goddamn thing I put in my mouth. I felt enough guilt for all of the friends who proved themselves to be only "fair-weather" and took the guilt from those who were genuinely good to me in an attempt to thank them for their kindness.
Guilt became my closest companion and left me with a heart that was heavy, absent of love, yet capable of loving so deeply. If I ever found myself feeling a certain way, an emotion or thought I was unfamiliar with - one that sat uncomfortably at the forefront of my mind - I would immediately resort to guilt to drown it out.

Slowly, it became easier to wallow in the negativity than it did to fight it. I didn't have the energy, I was exhausted. In my frantic attempts to subdue the emotions; my fear of not belonging anywhere or to anyone, the guilt at absolutely everything and anything, my body-dysmorphia and the way everything seemed to find its core in my simply not being good enough, I realised that being sad was to be my new normal. It wasn't an everyday sort of sadness. It wasn't staying inside and sleeping all day, self-harming or developing toxic eating habits. No, I had done all of that before. This was something different.

I was eating more because I was working more but, having a relationship with food that isn't considered stereotypically normal or healthy, I just saw an increase in consumption as an indulgence, rather than a physical necessity. I was too tired to fight the feelings of guilt, and so I became trapped in a vision of my body I just came to hate every single day, rather than only after eating a larger meal or taking a rest day from the gym. Rest days soon ceased to exist, but still, the self-criticism continued. Self-hate became the soundtrack to my everyday – the mixtape of my domestic existence and, in a futile attempt to drown out the feeling ever so slightly, I covered my mirrors with scarves and photographs so as to avoid accidentally glimpsing my reflection. It did not work. The dysmorphia became who I was. I had accepted there was no way that that was going to change any time soon and so, with a black mind and a chest full of debilitating melancholy, I sank slowly, a deflated red balloon, all the way back down the rabbit hole.

My sadness was "active".

To avoid my busy head, I had to have a busy life and in throwing myself into people, purpose and persistent routine, it allowed me to dwell in a constant state of blue without having to think about why. I stopped trying to pull myself out of the spiral and I let it suffocate me. I was living in a perpetual sigh, the type that comes from the bottom of your lungs and dredges every weary woe up with it, its cleansing never truly freeing me of the feeling of hopelessness. I could feel the kiss of tears behind my eyes but, for some reason, they never seemed to make themselves tangible. It was an ache for some form of healing, but the remedy seemed so far out of my reach that I decided to just accept that there was nothing I could do to change it. In its constancy I found comfort, as illogical as that sounds. Days would start the same and end the same and blend into one another like myriads of watercolour. But these weren't coloured in kaleidoscope. They were every shade of grey and black and deep navy blue - the only vibrancy I found was in the occasional spot of sunshine. The warmth would dapple my face whenever I stepped outside to commence whatever mission I was on - to distract myself from my self – and, in those moments of light, I would, just for a split second, embrace the calm.

Though I had grappled with 'The Numbness' for years, for some reason it started to preoccupy my every waking moment. Until, one day, it didn't.

The tempo of self-deprecation fused with my frustration at an inability to raise myself out of a new kind of desperate sorrow and, one Friday afternoon in early January, it reached its crescendo. I could try and describe the sensation as I walked home from work – sent home early because we had been so quiet – but I don't think I will ever be able to capture it. It was like nothing I had ever experienced in my life.

Instead of walking straight down the street, all the way to the gym as per my usual routine, I turned right towards the bus station.
Towards my house.

My legs carried me in motion absent of cognitive control - traipsing forward, driven by an unfamiliar impulse – I was straying so far from my usual routine, but I no longer exercised any agency over my physical movements. In my helplessness, I knew that something was about to change, what exactly was beyond me, but at this point, there was absolutely nothing I could do to stop it.

I was present but I wasn't present.

As I walked down the steps towards number fourteen, I felt as if someone had stuffed my head with cotton wool. It was a dense nothingness that deadened any residual cycling and spiralling of irrational thoughts. The angry knots that I had become so used to occupying every waking moment, the relentless hum of fraught tinnitus thought, was all of a sudden muffled.

Muted by a thick cloud of emptiness.

Somewhere, some part of me knew that what I was about to do would be something I would regret, something I wouldn't be proud of, something that would make me feel so utterly and hideously ashamed that I would never be able to repeat it to anyone, not even my mother, but I had given up. There was no changing my mind. The tears I had felt building, the pressure behind my tired eyes, began to slowly eb and bloom beneath my eyelids. My chest tightened and I could sense the rising hurricane of panic start to tornado in my gut. It washing-machine-ed its way into every cell, every muscle, every bone and I had absolutely no way of stopping it. It was a cyclone and in its rise to arms, I found myself knocking at the door of rock bottom, again.

All of a sudden, the cloud span into a frenzied black and, as soon as I stepped through the door, it started.
Self-harm was not something I had engaged in since my days in the inpatient unit. The ritualistic punching of thighs, head and stomach after mealtimes was now a low point only recalled in the memory of bruises that had softly disappeared.

Muscle memory is very real and so I knew what I was doing.

Fists and flesh and flesh and fists. Again and again and again and again. Fingers pulling at skin and muscle and all I could see was fat.

Fat. Fat. Fat.

It drummed in my head and ached through my heart, a broken record spitting out this singular, monosyllabic chant. It was as if every emotion I had compartmentalised into the 'Do-Not-Open' annexe of my mind had suddenly chimed into a choir. A satanic one.

The agony of desolation so potent that the physical pain was anaesthetised.

This was dysmorphia, crippled with sheer fatigue. Loneliness coloured the feeling monochrome and in my overflowing consciousness I was rendered empty. Hysterically, I rocked myself on the bed. My sister tried to calm me over the loudspeaker on my phone - but all I heard was white noise, echoed in sobs that ripped right through me to my core. I moved from the bedroom to the bathroom and back again. On the floor, perched on the toilet seat, back to the bed, just

r o c k i n g.

I was alone. All the people I had used to fill me were gone and in their absence the sadness had built and brimmed and bubbled. It had infected me. Manifested itself in the fabric of my being until I couldn't take anymore and, over I went. I fell. I tumbled. I drowned. I sank.

No, I was sinking.

Sinking into a low I had known was nearby but that I had danced precariously around as if engaging in some form of twisted game. Words have always been my way of making sense of the world; of my thoughts, my feelings and my body, but I do not think there are any words to truly describe how it felt to exist in that explosion of a moment. I could try, I suppose. I could construct a description, verbose, poignant and so detailed that maybe, just maybe, you could steal a glimpse into the tempest. But sometimes, it is in the simplicity of a sentence that we are able to feel it the most. It is why when I say I felt numb, I felt nothing. That when I felt sad, I felt only the colour blue. It is why, when I say I lost control, I really truly lost control - corkscrewing into midnight oblivion and experiencing a pain which gutted me till I was raw. This was a sensation, a junction in my life. One I wouldn't wish on my worst enemy but one which, in its all-consuming trauma, was essential in order for me to finally break what had become a toxic and monotonous cycle.

When I had finally come around, about two and a half hours later, my body had gone into shock. I could not cry, I did not have the capacity. I was dehydrated and my temples throbbed with the tension which had thrummed against my skull. I couldn't move my head more than an inch off the mattress and so I lay there, in silence, listening to my heart slow and finding solace in its softening pound. I was not sure what had just happened. It was like waking up from a general anaesthetic, caught in the remnants of a dream so lucid it seemed impossible for it to have happened. My reactions were delayed and so was the pain. The physical pain.

As my eyes started to blink themselves back into the softening light of sunset, my senses began to return to their rightful places. Fingertips tingling, then palms, a surge of energy raced through my veins and arteries, colouring my limbs with a new life, a new sensitivity to being. Down my shoulders and into my torso, an electric stream brought with it, not only feeling, but the reality of what I had done. My stomach was the last part to regain its responsiveness and when it did, it was with a stinging flutter. I pulled myself up. I was wrapped in a towel wearing only my underwear, and standing in front of the mirror. My lower belly was marbled purple. Bruises from where I had jerked and squashed and gripped the flesh were now stretching in lilac tributaries across the waistband of my pants. I stared, the flutter now making sense to me and with the return of logic came sharp shards of a smarting which marked the grand re-entrance of reality. I quickly covered them and inspected the rest of my body. The same small dark marks peppered my thighs, biceps and forehead – anger and frustration fingerprinting indigo smudges with the self-control and discipline of a tantrum-ing child. My cheeks were pink. They had managed to escape the extent of fist-to-flesh attention that my other, ampler extremities had fallen victim to, but still remained flushed in the rosy glow of shame.

Shame.

I was ashamed of the person that stood in front of me, not because of what she had done to herself, but for allowing herself to get to that point. The pain and the patterns that decorated my skin were not part of a mindful masterpiece. Their brushstrokes bore no conscious agency for they were angry contortions of a troubled psyche made manifest with no consideration for consequence. It was shame at relapsing into habits I had kicked so very many years ago, a part of my past I had buried in the hope that never again would I feel the heat of hate like that. It was shame that eviscerated me, that left no room for anything other than the stark visual reality of what I had done, but it was also a sense of shame that was superseded by another feeling, a sense of an ending.

The promise of a rebirth.

In my catharsis, I felt like I was floating, the little red balloon now tentatively reaching towards a sky that seemed so much clearer than before.
Everything that had weighed upon me, the relevant irrelevances which had driven me forward through every day, was now gone. Just g o n e.
In its absence I felt full of a content emptiness. I began to hunger for the satiation of my soul, but not with the affirmation of others. Instead, I wanted to nourish it with the excitement of discovery. Of embracing and engaging in the journey to self-discovery rather than seeing it as an end point, a goal.

When a person is able to cut the cord and enjoy the euphoria of independent flight, that is when they freefall. For me to realise the beauty of existing in a mind and body that wasn't obsessed with figuring out who she was, I had to clear the fog inside of my head. I had to stop relying on the chute and, instead, take pleasure in the liberation of living in the unknown.
The space I had filled with a tumbleweed of
Anxieties
Guilt
Broken promises
False friendships
Fears
Unresolved issues
An incessant and inane inability to address what I was most truly afraid of
- the person I saw reflected back at me -
was all of a sudden,   bare.

In its emptiness I found happiness, for I was clean and I was exposed and I was vulnerable. I was bared down to my very simplest form in all of the very best ways.

I remembered what it was like to be part of the world. I grounded myself in what I could see and smell and touch and feel. I started to walk every day and enjoyed being able to move to my own rhythm, to let my feet take me where they wanted rather than where I forced them to. I still went to the gym, but I found myself going a different way home rather than the same wearisome bolt there-and-back-and-there-and-back again, twice a day.
I pottered around, sometimes stopping and sitting in the sunshine, letting it wash over my face and dapple it in freckled fire. I stopped making people

the focus of every waking thought. I realised that it was OK to be alone and that independence is not ignorance. When it rained I looked up to the sky and smiled. I let the water collect on my eyelashes and drip off the tip of my nose. I was comforted in the chill of sleet and snow and hail, because it made me feel alive and present.

The sensation of existing was exhilarating.

The smell of the earth as Spring released her scent was addictive and, on my walks along the Lade Braes, I watched the green turn purple and white and yellow with each afternoon's passing wander. The smells symphonied around my peaceful mind and I became just as familiar with honeysuckle as I did the perfume I spritzed my skin with every morning. Light fascinated me and, instead of walking with my face turned towards a tiny screen, typing frantically...I started looking up.

Instead of desperately trying to find the reassurance I needed that everything was going to be alright from other people - these thoughts and these spirals and these feelings and this guilt that I had allowed to preoccupy and overwhelm me for years – I discovered that, by living and existing in that exact singular and instant moment, I could figure it out for myself.

In fact, a lot of the time, it didn't need to be figured out.

They were irrational thoughts that simply required realisation. I learnt how to rationalise without being wholly dependent on another to do it for me. My head had emptied of its irrelevant concerns and now I was able to take the thought – whatever dark, twisted futile fear it may be – and break it down, a problem with an almost instantaneous solution now I possessed the capability to view it pragmatically.

Just like I struggled to find the words to describe the sensation I felt when everything came to its head in January, I have tried (many a time) to do the same with the change I have experienced since. The early months of 2020 saw a new version of me emerge. She was more settled. Calmer.

I was experiencing a wholly different way of living, of interacting with the world as I submersed myself in it. The novelty of occupying a clear head was delicious.

In this absence of frivolous concerns, fears for universal belonging and a desire to be loved by anyone and everything, I allowed the spirit of who I was to start to filter through. I realised what I liked and what I didn't. I drank red wine and ate chocolate on days that weren't Fridays. I stopped counting calories and allowed myself rest days from exercise for the first time in eight years. I struck up conversations with complete strangers and I acted on impulse because it felt good to be spontaneous. I stopped overthinking every second thought and I became in touch with my body, just as much as I did my mind. I was kissed in the rain. I cried because I was happy, not because I was sad.

I laughed from my belly and spoke from my heart. I didn't censor my opinions for I spoke to people with views just as strong and I listened and I learnt from them, a new perspective of the world now colouring my attitudes in a palette of renewed vibrance, of unique hybrids. I had countless conversations with myself – self-reflection no longer a foreign and forbidden concept - and spent hours daydreaming. The fear of indulging in my imagination was long forgotten and, instead, I flourished in it.

Jane had needed to break before she could fix herself – before she could heal.

January 2020 was a low point, but the Little Red Balloon emerged from it as a phoenix does from ashes. The next two months saw her reconnect with the world in a way she had forgotten and, in letting go of all her remnant regrets, guilt and irrational fears, she started to craft the version of herself that was unapologetically honest and true.

She had finally let Zak go. She promised herself that never again would she let lust cloud her judgement or that she would sacrifice the inherent parts of her personality and who she was in order to please another person. If she couldn't be true to her mind then what sort of life was she living? She no longer wanted to occupy a skewed reality; it was toxic and oppressing and she only had a limited amount of time left in her beloved "bubble" so why waste it with fake friends and people that sucked the life out of her, rather than encouraging the balloon to soar.

She began to savour every day and, in doing so, she made some of her finest memories.

She experienced the excitement of falling in love, again.
She met a Canadian boy who saw beyond her surface the moment he sat

beside her on a bus back from St Albans in the early hours of a Sunday morning. He shocked her with his eloquence, and his charisma was as warm as his smile. He walked her home in cold Spring rain. He picked her up, swung her into his arms, and he kissed her. He made her feel spontaneous and she liked it. It was a brief first meeting and she didn't think much of it when he returned to London eight hours later, but fate is a funny thing and the world works in the strangest of ways.

She recalibrated her domestic life.
She gained a flatmate from Australia and he greeted her every morning with a 'good mornin' beautiful' or 'how you feelin' today sexy?' which made her smile. She couldn't remember the last time someone had thrown that sort of casual compliment at her. It was simple but it instilled in her a confidence she had suffocated for a long time.

She survived a global pandemic.
She turned twenty-four amidst the height of the 'Lockdown' and, in her isolation, she became content with being alone, once again. Yes, she spent hours writing letters and Facetiming friends, but she also spent twelve hours each day listening to music, reminding herself of the joy that exists in a language whose assonances and intricacies and quirks and lilts all tipple into conversations created through harmony. Words that are notes, played on keys and strings. Sentences formed out of, perhaps, the most honest kind of art. Emotions unapologetically and uncensoredly transposed into sound. The eloquence of constructed thought, not spoken, but strung.

She did not have a chance to say all the goodbyes she wishes she could have. To give all of the hugs and teary squeezes that usually come with farewells and 'see-you-laters', but she made the best of a bad situation and, when the time came, she tried to leave St Andrews with no ends left untied.

An Extract from Jane's Diary
March 2020

I had to say goodbye, bluntly and abruptly, to the two places I had come to call my home away from home. All of a sudden I went from running between jobs, apron strings tangling around my ankles as I sprinted up Market Street from the café to the bar, to having absolutely no job at all. No one needed me to bake banana loaf or toast sandwiches. No one needed me to pour pints or empty bottle bins. No-one messaged me asking about changing shifts or told me off for spilling red wine all over my work shirt. My mornings were suddenly empty hours to be filled with solitary contemplation. The familiar faces I had come to call friends, people I would see every day and natter to about the weather or the weekend, were gone without so much as a 'see you later'. Amidst the panic that ensued amongst my fellow co-workers as they faced the prospect of an indefinite lack of income, I desperately tried to figure out how I would exist without these people and this purpose structuring my days. Money just seemed irrelevant and insignificant. My opportunities to create new memories with them were invaluable and now they were gone.

When Jane left number fourteen on the 31st of May, she left with a heart full of love. She had no regrets when it came to St Andrews, because, though the first three years had been ones spent clinging onto a doomed relationship, the next three had allowed her to blossom into the truest version of herself.

Though it had been far from easy and the pathway had seemed almost impossible at times, Jane reversed down the driveway of Miller's Road as a woman, not a girl. A woman who had overcome anorexia – twice. A woman that who was not dependent on Sertraline in order to lift her spirits. A woman who was happily single, independent and not afraid to speak her mind or have her own opinions. A woman who had mastered her anxiety – at least to some extent – and a woman with (nearly) two degrees to her name. A woman who was no longer afraid of sex or intimacy and a woman who had, against all odds, fought her way through depression and the paralysis of all-consuming guilt.

In staying in St Andrews, she had thrown caution to everything, but it had made her time there, her St Andrews "Chapter", one of rather spectacular growth. It had set the highest of bars for the next instalment of Jane's life, and had made all of the struggle, the pain and the heartache of the years that had gone before it, seem worth every single second.

Chapter 13
Still Being Written...

Hello. My name is Megan Jane Ravenhall and this was (and is) my story.

I told you, right at the beginning, that this story would have thirteen chapters. The thirteenth is still being written, and so here I am, writing it, as promised.

You may wonder why I did not tell you my name. Why I did not tell you the story just as it came out of my head and tapped itself into my keyboard. Why I chose to write it about "a girl" rather than as the girl that I once was - who I suppose I still am, deep down.

I didn't tell you my name because I wanted you to hate Jane. I wanted you to cry with her. I wanted you to laugh with her. I wanted you to go through her journey and watch her fall, but then share the euphoria of her rise, each and every time.

I was Jane. I am Jane, just as I was anorexia and anorexia became me.

But then I ate a carrot.

I remembered how to smile and how to laugh. I ran around reservoirs in the snow on my own two feet. I taught myself how to eat again and I recalibrated a mind that had got lost in the darkness for so long that I didn't think I would ever blink in the light again.
I have run two half-marathons – both in aid of Beat and the inpatient and paediatric wards that saved my life. I have run a marathon, purely because my body could. I have completed Tough Mudder and hitchhiked from Glasgow to Madrid. I have been a baker, a bartender, a barista and a chef.

I have had my heart broken again and again and again. I have lost myself trying to be someone I wasn't – trying to fit a mould that I thought would please a person on whose affection (or lack thereof) I was dependent, in the absence of any I had for myself. I have relapsed, and forgotten who I was in the process. It took me a year, but, I reclaimed my identity. I have found myself battling mental illness in more than one form. I have been sad for months and euphoric for days. I have realised that it is OK to be alone and, that being alone is actually incredibly liberating.

I had to put my trust in the universe and immerse myself in life, in order to see that I was a person - a soul, a body and a mind - in my own right. Someone that did not actually need anyone. My identity was not dependent on someone else's opinion of me and, in my enlightenment, I gained the gift of content loneliness.

A person that knows they can exist alone is never actually lonely.

I have smoked and I have drunk. I have tried hypnotherapy and mindfulness. I have been vegan, gluten-free, vegetarian, pescatarian, but never quite managed Keto. I have listened to music – live and on the radio. I have been to Balls – too many to count – in my wellies and in heels and in a pair of sliders I picked up from under the bar on one occasion for reasons that I was too drunk to recall. I have climbed the CN tower and have seen Niagara Falls. I have visited the home of my very first imaginary friend, 'Hogsmeade' in Orlando, and drunk butterbeer whilst perusing 'Olivander's Wand Shop'.

I have seen my sister meet the love of her life, gained another brother in the process and watched the two of them prove to me that love is not dependent on shape or size or looks – it is the unconditional type of passion and adoration that comes from knowing a person at their very worst and at their very best, but still loving them just the same.

I have seen my baby brother turn into one of the most sensitive and emotionally intelligent people I have ever had the pleasure to meet. Though he winds me up like no one else can, I have found myself overwhelmed with admiration and a pride that blooms in my chest every time he records a podcast or performs stand-up comedy.

I have realised that my body is capable of so much more than I give her credit for and, in allowing her to heal, I was able to test and trial her like one might a car. I have jumped off piers and skinny dipped in the icy waves of early spring mornings on the beach. I have built bonfires on the sand and made s'mores – the Carolina way. I have pulled pints and poured feathers into espresso out of frothed milk. I have hosted potlucks for all of my friends on Sundays and held pre-drinks before messy Friday nights out. I have cried at work and I have laughed at work and I have become a part of a very different type of family, well, two actually.

My "Bar family" was formed out of a shared frustration at drunken students. It was maintained through end-of-shift sweaty hugs that stank of spilt sambuca and was immortalised in the late-night munchies and waves of exhausted acknowledgment when we bumped into one another at the gym the next day. My "Café family" saw bonds crafted in weary early-morning smiles, sleepy morning faces brightened quickly through a squeeze of a hug and a strong cuppa. The hysterical tears of laughter that were shed over spilt milk became our lifeblood and the ties between barista and boss went far beyond our café door.

I have had the odd one-night stand (or two) and relationships that have lasted a mere month. I have kissed girls and I have kissed boys. I've been gaslighted and emotionally abused, but I have also been swept off my feet – both literally and metaphorically. I have sat next to strangers on buses and felt a closeness of connection I haven't experienced with friends of a lifetime. I have realised that, just as happiness is something that can be experienced in a singular moment or as an extended euphoria, so too, is love.

I have experienced moments of love with fierce intensity but, thus far in my life, I have only ever been in love, once. I have broken two hearts - one I wish so desperately I could heal. I have felt things I wish I hadn't and confused love with lust too many times that I care to mention, but I would not change a single choice or mistake I made, for it taught me how to be a better person. It taught me how to love in a way free of romantic expectation or idealisation. It was a love that was
momentary
and spontaneous
and fun!

I have tried to learn to play guitar and failed. I have succeeded in mastering the art of the perfect fudge brownie, but white chocolate blondies are something which still fail me. I have shaved my head and I have cut my own hair – regretting my decisions every time, but doing it again and again nonetheless. I have acted on impulse and I have hurt the people I love the most, but I realised and I apologised and I used it to help me grow, as a daughter, sister, girlfriend and friend.

I have grown into myself, not as Jane, but as Megan for this remarkable thing we call "Life" is about stepping stones.

The little hop-skip-jumps of the everyday, those that eventually lead us to achieving our objectives or realising our dreams, often actually turn out to be the biggest. I believe that people should be there to pick you up if you topple ever so slightly. They should be waving you on from the side lines and sharing the joy you feel when you land – two feet forward – sturdy and set on the next wobbly rock leading towards the shore of personal aspiration. They should be part of your journey, but they should not determine its outcome, because knowing yourself is not something other people can teach you. This higgledy-piggledy trail through the water is a pathway to self-acceptance and maybe even self-love. The knocks and scrapes and scratches we collect along our way form scars of self-development and, amidst the turbulence which may flood the simplest route, we will find a new way of venturing forward, even if it is a more precarious balancing act at times.

A sense of self-actualisation may occur at any point along the journey, whether it be at one of the slips or mid-leap. I thought that I had found mine after dragging myself back up from the rapids for the millionth time, yet still I learn more about myself every day. In all honesty, the person who sits writing this, remains clueless to the essence of who she actually is. I know that it is possible to resurface, that in fact, it is inevitable, but it can seem impossible and, trust me when I say, I feel that impossibility every day. If I have learnt anything, however, it is that, though the leap may seem hellishly intimidating, one cannot let the fear of falling determine each and every step because, sometimes, the fall is the very best part.

Yes, I relapsed.
But only *once*.

I gained two stone in two months because I was happy and I was free and I stopped caring about the calories and started focusing on the memories. I graduated. I wrote off my car. I bought a new one and I called her Lola. When I wanted to feel alive I drove her fast on country lanes with the roof down, music so loud the bass made my chest rumble.

I had breakdowns, many, and at times I forgot who I was – what all of this had been for, but it didn't make me weak. It made me human.

Being human is not easy.

Knowing yourself is one thing, remaining true to it, another.

Every single day we wake up and there is a body stretching out in front of us. Feet that have walked millions, maybe even billions of steps. Knees that are scratched and scarred from all of the bumps and tumbles we have each and every day. Hips that may have born children or seen metal replace bone. A stomach that has the propensity to experience every cuisine and culture under the sun. A chest that has battled flus and infections with lungs that have smoked tobacco and 'green' in equal measure. A liver that has been subjected to alcohol's wicked yet wonderful way and a heart that has felt love and pain and joy and anger in every shade of colour, all at once and not at all. Arms that have wrapped themselves around friends and family, hands that have held others, speaking those three simple words in a way that voices cannot. Fingers that have made melodies out of ivory and strung harmony out of string. Nails bitten till they are raw from nerves and knuckles that have met flesh in fits of rage. A neck that has been tie-dyed violet in a passing lover's passion, ears that have heard all manner of conversations matched with mouths which have proffered their very own 'tuppence' in return. A nose that has been broken and bled and dusted white off of £20 train tracks. Lips that have been cracked and kissed and have conversed. Teeth, chipped and stained, yellow then white and yellow again. Fillings flung out after a particularly tasty toffee and a tongue that has been burnt too many times, the perpetual victim of desperate sips of coffee or biscuits stolen right out of the oven. Eyes that have seen everything, and sometimes, nothing. Irises that change colour when sunlight hits them in that one specific spot. Pupils that have dilated with all manner of stimuli, exposing the sensations of a body unable to control its pain or pleasure. A head that has ached with hangovers, hummed with dozy Sunday afternoon calm or buzzed with the chaos of frantic attempts to remember seventeen things at once.

This body is technically what makes us human. It acts as our engine and enables us to do that thing we call existing.

What makes us truly human though, is how we view and interact with the world, through our emotions, physical sensations, the way our mind works, our choices, our victories or our defeats.

In our world, being human is not simple. It is completely and utterly absurdly complicated but, being human, in all its glorious ups and downs and "ins and outs", is all we can ever ask for ourselves. For, when we are true to the person who occupies the body that holds together all the parts that make us human, that is when we achieve a state of being that isn't purely existing.

It is l i v i n g.

Something I never truly knew to be the case until it was and now it is all it will ever be.

I do not know if I will ever be able to love this body of mine, but I am getting better at being kind to it. I am lucky, so very lucky, that I have so many people in my life that love me for me. I would not be here today if it wasn't for that love. That faith. That hope.

My story is my miracle.

Recovery is not easy. Just when you think you are out of the woods, something can swoop in and knock you for six, as is proven in the journey of Jane. My whole life, I have felt things – feelings, thoughts, emotions – with an intensity that has made attachments easy to form and farewells seem almost impossible. For a long time, I thought it more of a curse than a blessing – possessing so much love, but never really feeling it reciprocated, or at least thinking I wasn't worthy of its return, except when it came from family. Even then, I struggled to understand why someone could love me as much as my parents or my siblings did – it just didn't seem logical to me, yet I threw so much of my own heart at people I barely knew without question.

Anorexia didn't ask me for love. She didn't tell me I was beautiful or that I was a strong and fierce young woman. She told me I was ugly and fat and worthless and stupid. She hated me and, in some sick, twisted way, her hatred brought me a greater sense of fulfilment than any outward displays of love or affection I received from others ever could. For me, self-hatred was so much easier to process than self-love. In hating every part of myself, there was no pressure to maintain the "good" parts, because, if everything was "bad", then I could just dwell in a constant state of you-are-not-and-never-will-be-good-enough-and-that-is-that. Every time something good would happen, I would find a way to ruin it – I was self-destructive to my core and it all stemmed from not feeling worthy of those tiny pockets of happiness that occur when you least expect them to. Anorexia promised me a way of dealing with a world I was terrified of exploring alone, a world that I wasn't sure I deserved a place in. She was my companion when life got too much, because she reminded me that when all else failed, there was one constant – one thing I would always be able to control – and that constant was food.

I thought being "skinny" would make me happy. I hit a weight that was so low it nearly killed me but, even then, I still thought I was "fat".

When it comes to anorexia, there is never a point at which a person will be skinny enough to satisfy the critical voice inside their head. It is a pursuit in search of an unattainable reward, because, even when your organs are failing and your bones are breaking and every line on your face is just another mark on the Hangman's sketch, you will never be happy. I promise you – there is no such thing. Being skinny "enough" is so far beyond impossible that words will never truly capture the desperate and shocking reality of it.

The myth of "ultimate thinness" is beyond impossible, because impossible spells 'I'm possible' and, to put it bluntly, it simply is not.

I was told that recovering fully from my eating disorder was impossible – I made it possible. I was told going to university in 2014 was impossible – I made it possible. I am possible, because I am Megan and Megan realised that she could achieve the impossible if she put her mind to it. Being so skinny you are finally happy is not impossible, it is beyond impossible, because the only way you will achieve it is when you are so malnourished that you are dead – a corpse – and corpses cannot taste anything. Corpses are absent of life.

Weight was the one thing I "thought" I could control. I couldn't control my emotions or the way I felt about certain people and certain things. I couldn't control the weather just like I couldn't seem to control my mood. The way it would swing in its pendulum motion between happy and sad, depressed and overjoyed, was just as erratic as the shifting seasons. What I could master, however, was my weight but, even then, I was never truly satisfied with the number. I strived for something too unrealistic, too unfathomably unachievable, something that existed beyond impossible. The lower my weight got, the further away the promised land where skinny tasted better than any food became. As a result, I was constantly sad, because I thought that I would only be happy – or at least allow myself to be momentarily - when my goal had been reached.

I was wrong.

Being skinnier than your natural body shape does not make a person happy. It does not make them feel warm and light and lovely inside. Yes, it may be the genetic body shape for some – those with high metabolisms or natural genetics – but for those of us for whom it is not, it is unhealthy and wrong for us to force our bodies to take on a form that they naturally are not meant to have. It is like squeezing a jigsaw piece into a hole that you know it won't fit or trying to reach the top shelf of a supermarket aisle when it towers a good three feet
above you. My mother once told me that the longer we stare at our reflections, the more faults we will see - if you look at anything for long enough, you will be always be able find something not quite perfect – and she was right.

Life is not perfect and neither are human beings. Each fault we identify has the power to lower a person's spirits, to challenge an already dwindling self-esteem. Therefore, what if, instead of allowing these spots or wrinkles or chubby cheeks to make us feel cripplingly self-conscious, instead we accept that they are what make us perfectly imperfect?

This was something I only truly understood when I realised that, actually, there are certain times in life when the closer you look, the more magic you see. For my twenty fourth birthday, two friends of mine bought me a planetarium, perhaps the greatest gift I have ever received. As I lay in my bed watching the stars shoot across a galaxy crafted out of electricity and light, I felt humbled to be a part of something that was so big and bold and beautifully beyond the tiny presence that was my own existence. The longer and the closer I looked, the more stars I saw. They moved slowly, glittering across the arcing galaxy, thousands of wonderfully unique pockets of quiet brightness. Little lights, pulsing white. It made me think. Rather than seeing each star as a mark - a blemish on the canvas of the sky - each and every one should be celebrated for its glow, for its modest contribution to the magnificence of the perfectly imperfect projection as a whole.

Just as trees may simply be green and the sunshine, yellow, this black and white universe made me appreciate that it truly is a wonderful world we occupy, because nothing ever is 'just so'. If we are to look closer, that green is made up of a million different shades of emerald – it changes colour with the seasons; green becomes gold and then soft, earthy brown. And the sun? Oh, she is so much more than mere yellow. She is fire. Things change just as people change, for we are the product of our experiences – we learn from our mistakes and our bodies adapt to the circumstances and environments we subject them to. It is a fact of our existence. Our faces develop lines to remind us of the laughter and the joy we have experienced over the years. The sunshine douses our foreheads in freckles with each passing summer. Our time is limited, so why do we choose to let the negatives outweigh the positives so very often? Our imperfections come partnered with memories, whether it be a spot from one weekend of heavy drinking with friends or a scar on our chin from the time we fell off our bike. As my friend, Ailia, told me, the curves on our bodies are formed out of love. These little pieces are what make us extraordinary and we should never take them for granted, never mind allow them to dictate our mood or plans.

* * *

To anyone reading this who may be struggling, I beg of you – ask for help – you are so much more than the voice inside your head tells you you are. Do not give in to the blackness.

To those of you who are making your first tentative, but wonderfully brave steps into recovery, have faith in yourself and you will emerge victorious. If you submit to the voices, you will become a victim once more; you will render yourself helpless. Life is too short to be a victim, especially to your own mind. It is too short not to eat avocado toast and lick sticky ice-cream fingers with friends. Food is not like sex, or drugs or alcohol, though, at times, our relationship with any of these can become skewed and squinted. Unlike the others, food is integral to our survival – you don't have to love eating, but you must do it, for if you don't, living becomes existing and existing is no life – that I can promise.

To the families, friends and partners – you are not to blame. There is a reason you come under the bracket of "loved one" and that is because, no matter what, you are loved. Even if we yell and scream and curse and lash out with the most venomous and spiteful tirades – we love you and we need you, but we desperately want you to understand why we are acting the way we are. It is not our choice, it is our curse. You try so hard to use the knowledge you get from books and websites and doctors but, ultimately, you cannot possibly understand why we think the way we do because you are not inside our heads.

This is why I wrote the story of the Little Red Balloon, so that you might gain an insight into the psyche of an anorexia sufferer and so that you may be armed with understanding, rather than the basic facts. To comprehend is to support in a way I personally believe to be pivotal in guiding a sufferer towards the pathway of recovery. It is why this story is dedicated to my Mum, because she is the greatest, most empathetic and truly understanding individual I have ever met.

Mum knows me better than I know myself, including the darker parts of me. Though she has never struggled with an eating disorder, I dragged her through mine from the very root of the nightmare and I genuinely believe that she is an expert in my illness, just as I believe I am. Well, in the experience part of it anyway.

Words are how I make sense of the world. They are how I tell people I love them and how I show them I do not. When I try and find the words to describe how grateful I am to my Mum for everything she has done for me, I cannot, because there are none. Occasionally, it is in the simplicity of a phrase that we capture the most honest truth and, when I say I love my Mum, I mean, I love my Mum. It is a love that goes beyond action, speech or thought. It is just there.

Simple.

I grew inside of her twenty-four years ago. She nourished me from that very first feed to the last Fortisip we drank together prior to my inpatient admission. She nursed me when I fell over and scraped my knee and she massaged my aching joints when the jolting wheelchair took its toll. She picked me up from school and she taught me how to drive. She calmed me when I had nightmares about the world ending and the universe collapsing and she held me close to her chest when I was overcome with such hatred for myself that all I wanted to do was inflict physical pain with tightened fists. She bought me my first Prom dress and she picks up the phone whenever I'm feeling even the slightest bit out of sorts. She knows when the self- hatred is weighing heavy on me, without my having to say a word and, when the memories return with lucid vengeance, she takes me out in the car and we drive until the fire trickling down my face dwindles into exhausted and steady sobs.

I am lucky that I had this woman, my Mum, to hold my hand every step of the way.

To all of the Mums that are reading this, to all of the Dads, to all of the sisters, brothers, girlfriends, boyfriends, grandparents, aunties, uncles and friends - reach out and take their hand.

You cannot possibly imagine how comforting and how wonderful that simple act of care and kindness can be.

Have hope, be kind and remember, mental illness is not a choice.

Recovery is, choose it.

$$* * *$$

A Letter to My Body - Extracts
10th January 2021
...
Sitting on the toilet seat, wrapped in a beige towel. Blue toothpaste stains from where I swiped my lips after the fifth time brushing my teeth today. All I do is drink is coffee and smoke cigarettes, so why I bother brushing them I do not know. A futile attempt to flush the yellow stains away. I sat there. Waiting for the doctor to call... perhaps an hour, perhaps forty-five minutes. I cried. Deep tears that burned the corners of my eyes. They dripped hot onto my bruised arms and joined the cold coconut wet that fell from my clean hair. I tried to look up but it was just too hard. I sobbed onto the blue stains until I stopped. I said 'I'm so sorry that I am doing this to you' staring at red knees. But then I realised that this I was not me, it was her. She was doing this and I was hurting and you were hurting and she was winning.

....

You are what carries me every single day. I nearly lost you once upon a time. She took you away from me and I was left with wheels. Wheels and the scars that now mark my spine. Scars from sit-ups on the floor of a hospital bathroom. I can still smell the soap they bought me the day I moved in. There was a set with lotion and scrubs and serums in it. It came in a big pink box and I lined them all up on the shelf when I had my first moment alone. It smelt so fake. I felt so fake. I would tell myself that every time I ate. You're a Fake. Well, I suppose it was her actually. She would tell me that I was a Fake. A fake anorexic and a fat one at that.

I'd do hundreds of them. The sit-ups. But, of course, you know this. Up and down, up and down on hard, white linoleum. I'd close my eyes and feel my spine and my coccyx knock against the floor. Like a car over a cattle grid. They felt like knuckles. Knuckles along my spine. Every morning and every evening, into the bathroom we would go. You, me, her. I've never been so clean in my life. Every time I could take a shower, I would. Running on the spot until I heard the knock on my bedroom door that it was time for yet more food. They didn't catch me, nope, not ever. They came close, a couple of times. They only found out because Mum told them. She saw the bruises and then that was that, a bathroom locked and no more sit-ups. For a while. We started them again at home. Cream carpet a little kinder to my spine. Until Alex caught us. Then they stopped. I still have the scars though. And the pink box that the soaps came in. I think it's under my bed. Full of cables and old headphones.

....

Maybe I am what I think I am.

On the phone, to the doctor, she asked me if I had had a period of extended euphoria. Had I been promiscuous, had I taken risks? I told her there had been a time when my friends thought I was on drugs I was so happy. I remember going out in the dark. It was misty and the fog was beautiful. I took strides so large I could have been flying. My feet moved so quickly and with such magic that I might have been dancing. I felt like I was. I slipped into the fog and I called everyone. I watched the moon and told them all that this was it. I was finally free. Free of her. Finally after seven years, it was just us. Me and you, my beautiful bold body. YOU. But then the shadows came and I fell from my high just as swiftly as I had danced my way through it. I miss the confidence that came with my happiness. I crave it when I slouch around in jumpers and sweats four times too big because the low isn't a place for sex. Nobody wants to see my body. You. Nobody wants to see you. Especially not me. My shattered mirror is a blessing when we feel like this. When I feel like this.

I wanted to call this black, but I do not think it is. My euphoria was black, this is grey. So very grey. And lonely. Grey and lonely. Sometimes it is red.

Red, when she tells me the things that make me want to hurt you. My body, you.

I cry every day. Every single day. It seems to be something that I just happen to do now. When I make my coffee or listen to the radio. Sometimes in the steam of the shower, I'll look up to the lights and I will cry. I'll hold myself and feel my rib cage and crumble and cry. It doesn't matter if it's been a good day or a bad one– though most days seem to fit the latter nowadays. I cried at the sunrise yesterday and yesterday I was happy. At least I was until I wasn't. We walked quite far yesterday, you and I. After I had gotten angry. After we had lain on the floor of the bathroom for a while. When I started to shiver we managed to get up and we pulled on a jumper and some pants and we went and we walked and we saw the sky turn purple and it was beautiful. Purple and lovely.

I haven't been able to write for a while. When I was in my euphoria I wrote so much. I was so happy and electric and alive. When I am in this grey I find it hard to do anything, anything other than walk.

And so, we walk.

Many, many miles. We listen to the same music, though now I've managed to organise the sounds into something that fits each mood. I called the playlists
high
low
and in-between
Though lately all I've played is low. Sometimes my day will start with high and end with low. Our day. When I am on the floor and I cannot move there is no music. Just me, talking to you whilst she sits on her pedestal and watches the pain that she catalyses so easily. Just a glance at my reflection or a simple word. Lazy. Fat. Worthless. Any and all. She plants the seed of a thought and then that is all that occupies until it grows into a hatred and then the hatred breaks its fists into you, my body, you. And then we cannot move and the crying comes again.

Sometimes it is gentle tears. Gentle constant tears. Sometimes they rip through me and they hurt just as much as the bruises. My chest starts to heave and my lungs burn and I ask her. I say it. 'Why are you doing this to me?'

But of course, she never replies. She is silent, for she is content.

* * *

12th of February 2021

Initially, I had thought about ending the story there. Right before my letter. Nice and pretty and neat, with that line 'Recovery is, choose it'. But, then I did a little bit more of that thing we call life and life did a little bit more of that thing where it throws curveballs.

I wrote this story with honesty as its focus. Like I said, there is no trigger warning, because this is not a story to be read and aspire to. This is a story about pain and life and people. People that made me choose life over anorexia. People that picked me up from the pit of depression. People that accompanied me on socially distanced walks along the beach amidst nationwide lockdowns. People that smiled with their eyes at me from across the street, their mask blocking their mouths.

People made me understand the importance of honesty because, for so long, I had lied to them. I was scared of telling the truth. Of letting this pretence of being OK, falter. When people asked me 'are you ok?' I said 'yes.'

Do you know how often I wanted to turn around and say
'No, actually, I'm not'?
But, like so many people, I was scared. Scared of telling the truth. I was scared of the shame that I associated with self-harm and sadness. I was scared of making someone else feel as uncomfortable as I was.
And so, I pretended.
I pretended when I went for coffee and I pretended when I went for drinks. I pretended every day at work and I pretended every night at dinner. I pretended because I thought that pretending would make them accept me, love me maybe. But then pretending became second nature and I forgot what it was not to pretend.

That was, until, I was at home with my family.
The people who knew my pretence of pretend was actually a scream for help.

I am not OK.

We should normalise saying it. So, I'll say it again.
I am not OK.

I wrote a book about learning to be OK. A book you have nearly finished.
A book you could have finished with an overwhelming sense of hope. I do
not want to take that hope away from you. Hope is still present in my life.
More now than ever before. I just suppose I want to instil a sense of hope
that is realistic hope. This book is my story. The story of learning to be OK
with my body and OK with my mind. OK with food and OK with exercise.
OK with saying no and OK with saying yes. But today, I choose to say that
no, I am not OK.

And that? That is OK.

It is OK not to be OK and knowing that, accepting that, is recovery, right
there.

Recovery and also, life.

A global pandemic happens and yet still, there is an overwhelming
expectation, an expectation we are all guilty of placing on ourselves, to
reply to that question 'yes, I am OK.'
Maybe it is because it is easier that way. But where is the fun in easy?

Try it next time. Try saying 'no' if 'no' is how you are feeling.
Forgive yourself.
It is OK if you are not OK. Having the bravery not to pretend, not to smile
and say 'yes, I'm alright', is liberation in its purest form.

I have my good days and I have my bad. But I am learning to talk about
the bad days just as I rave about the good. That is why I leave you with a
letter I wrote to my body. A letter composed in January 2021 after all of the
story had been written. The story so far that is.

I include this for you so that you might see that the pathway to recovery
is still bumpy. That the pathway of life is far from easy. For so long, I have
viewed my life as my recovery journey, but now, now I realised that
actually, maybe this is not recovery, maybe this is just life.

I once knew a man, a man who saw life as the greatest flirtation of them all. When things got a little wonky, he used to say to me 'that's just showbiz baby' and he was right. Recovery, life, whatever you choose to call the precious pocket of time that each and every one of us has on this planet, is never plain sailing but 'that's just showbiz' and it is why it's OK not to be OK. Good days, bad days, highs, lows, it is all part and parcel of the show. Be brave enough to say, 'I am not OK'. Be confident enough to say, 'yeah, I'm absolutely brilliant actually'.

Just please don't pretend, because pretending is not living.

People, love and pain. That's what makes life living. It is what makes us human.

Mental illness is not a choice. Living life to its fullest, is.
Flirt with her, love her, live her. Choose her.
Because when the lights come up and the showbiz ends, life is all we've got.

Thirteen thank yous

The last of the thirteens and perhaps the most important of them all, is the thirteen thank yous I owe to the people without whom this book would not have been written. Though some of you are, unfortunately, no longer in my life, I owe mine to you and for that I shall be forever grateful. These thank yous come from both Megan and Jane, because there are certain people who were there for Jane's story but never got to see Meg's, just as there are those who met Megan and never got to see Jane. Those people are still alive, but sometimes people choose different pathways and the time we do spend wandering in the same direction, does not mean that we will always walk that road together.

1. Mum
This entire book is dedicated to you but still, I do not think I will ever be able to show you how grateful I am for everything you have done for me. Thank you, for it all. For saving my life, for helping me heal and for being there every step of the way – literally through thick and thin. You are the strongest woman I know and the love you have shown me, throughout my life, has saved me, too many times to count. You taught me that no matter what life throws at me, there is always a light, there is always hope, and there is always you - you who love me unrequitedly, irrevocably and completely. You who are proud of me for simply still being alive. I always used to think that the notion of "soul mates" was reserved for explicitly romantic relations, but the more I reflect on the depth of our connection, the more I think that you are mine.

2. Dad
I am not sure where to start with the thank yous that I owe you - there are too many. Thank you for the hours upon hours you have spent proof reading, editing and highlighting all of my dyslexic errors. Thank you for

putting up with every outburst and fit of hysterics and for never not loving me with the fierce pride and adoration that fathers do. You dedicated your MPhil to me and to Mum. I dedicate every single draft of this book to you for you have been there for every version of myself – the good, the bad, the ugly – and I love you more than you could ever possibly know. Thank you Dad, for being my real-life superman. One day we will be able to share a Wispa without me bursting into tears again, I am sure.

3. Rosie Posie
This is a thank you that goes, not only to my sister, but to my best friend. Life has given you quite the bunch of lemons, but, my oh my, have you turned those lemons into some pretty spectacular lemonade. You are a sunbeam, Rosie, and you bring so much light into everyone's lives with that smile of yours. You inspire me to be bolder, to speak my mind and to fight for what I believe in and the fire you hold inside you – that unapologetic pride in who you are – is infectious. Thank you, Rosie, for being the best little big sister a girl could ever wish for.

4. Alex
My little brother, Bertie. It's not been an easy road for you and me but age has become us and I think, finally, we have found our feet. I always wanted an older brother, someone to stand up to bullies for me, someone to be over-protective and pick me up from parties when I was sad and drunk and too scared to tell Mum and Dad. Instead, I was gifted you and I would not have it any other way. Alexander James, we are the same – neurotic, OCD, stress-fiends, sensitive and absolutely terrible at controlling our emotions - but that is what makes us, us. You have been all of the things I ever wanted from an older brother, and more, and you are the one boy I never have to fear will break my heart, for you have helped me to fix it, too many times for me to count.

5. Grandma
Again, I find myself at a loss to truly find the right words to express how grateful I am for you and everything you did to help save my life. I am sorry, Grandma, for all that I put you through, especially when you were trying to take care of Grandad at the same time. You have always been there - whether it be on the other end of the phone or pottering around your garden watering plants - and never fail to offer an ear when I need someone to talk to or require advice on absolutely anything and everything. I am so sorry for the deceit and the lies I told when I was in your care and for the additional sadness I brought to you and Grandad when

you already had so much to deal with. Thank you for never questioning me
and for just being those two wise old owls who could always find some
way of making me believe in the magic of miracles when all my faith had
gone.

6. Leen

Lovely Leen. Thank you for everything. You were the first person to read my
book from cover to cover, back when I called it Thirteen. You have been a
constant source of support and sunshine and I cannot express how greatly
I needed a friend and how perfectly you jumped straight into that role. You
are a diamond - one of the few people I have met that seems to struggle
with feeling such an intensity of emotion as me. Never, ever, change, for,
though it may feel like an impossible burden at times, your capacity to feel
is what makes you, you and it is wonderful.

7. Claire

This one is a big one.

Claire, when I met you back in September 2018, we were both starting
our first day at the Deli. I never would have thought that the friendship
which has blossomed since - between boss and barista - could become so
wholesome, but you proved me wrong. When I found out about this book –
something I have only really ever dreamed of – I knew, instantly, that it was
you who I wanted to design the cover. Your style of illustration is beyond
beautiful and the way that you have captured the essence of Jane's story
on the cover of this book is, in my eyes, perfect.

Thank you for taking care of me and buying me reduced chicken from
Tesco when you thought I wasn't eating properly. Thank you for the coffees
and the salads and the sandwiches. Thank you for giving me my job back
after I left for a wee while and thank you for being – and I mean this from
the very bottom of my heart – the closest thing to a mother that I ever could
have hoped for when I wasn't able to give my actual Mum a big squeeze.

8. Ella

Back when I knocked on a big blue door for a house viewing, many
moons ago, I saw you and instantly, I knew that you were just like me. I
was terrified at first. I worried that perhaps we would be less of a good
influence and more of a trigger for one another, but once again, I was
proven wrong. You encouraged me to speak, because I had a voice you
felt deserved to be heard. I had a story to tell and it was my duty to be

the change I wanted to see in the world. You told me that these bodies we called our own were ours and that was precisely why we should love them. I remember you telling me that recovery was like being inside a box. So long as you still straddled the side of it, you could fall back down, but as soon as you took that first step - that leap of faith into the space that existed outside the recovery "bubble", then life truly began and anorexia could be left behind. Wiser words have never been spoken. Your belief that the curves our bodies boast are a landscape we should celebrate, for they are the result of memories made out of love, is something I hold on to when the days are a little darker and dysmorphia wracks my reflection. Thank you for being The Mill's very own miracle. Never stop shining, my little Scottish star.

9. Reed
I met you towards the end of my time in St Andrews, but I could not have survived the second wave of the pandemic without you. Thank you for being my "person" and by person I mean "life-line". I do not think I have ever confided in someone the way I have confided in you and your support has kept me floating whenever the darkness has started to suffocate me again. You rationalise my irrational thoughts, reason with my unreasonable behaviours and give hugs that cure the soul in some sort of way I just cannot put into words. Thank you for being you, I appreciate you, never forget it.

10. Friends from "The Bubble"
Well, to put it bluntly, you made living, living.

It takes a certain group of people to make a person want to stay in the same place for such a long time. Sometimes, it takes many. Every year I spent in St Andrews, I met someone new – someone with a new story, someone with a new smile, someone with their own group of friends for whom I found a new affinity – and that is why I struggled so hard to leave.

Thank you for being the people that finally made me feel like I belonged, no matter what year or social circle you were in. You made me realise that I didn't have to devote all my time to a singular person to feel validated, appreciated or loved because friendship is a type of love in itself. Thank you for the memorably unmemorable nights spent drinking and the endless stream of Pret a Manger coffee dates. Thank you for lending me dresses and shoes so that I could attend Ball after Ball and throwing me hoodies from the bottom of your wardrobes when I forgot to bring a coat and it started to rain. Thank you for keeping me company on long day shifts at the bar – bringing me chocolate buttons when I was working a double shift – or, swinging into the Deli, atrociously hungover from the night before, to make me smile with tales of your hectic evening as you sat by the coffee machine watching me make flat whites and cappuccinos.

I wish I could name all of you but I think I shall let you preserve your anonymity for some of you are all still very present in my life and some of you, not so much. Whether you were there for a moment or there from the beginning all the way through to the end, that moment was no doubt spectacular and that long-haul, definitely worth the ride. Some of you I still speak to every day, some of you I don't, but, when you aren't by my side – dancing, drinking, smoking, laughing, nattering about nothing or speaking volumes in our happy silence – the memories we have made never fail to make my lips twitch into a smile and my eyes light up as if it were merely yesterday.

11. Dr E
I would not be here today without you. Thank you for helping the Little Red Balloon remember who she was. You met Jane, I only wish you had got to meet Megan but, unfortunately, our therapy sessions came to a close before I really came back into my own. It hasn't been easy, but you were right – with time comes peace, even if it can get a little tumultuous at times.

12. Belinda
Thank you for reading and believing. You made 'My friend, Jane.' a reality and for that I am still, to this day, rather speechless. You were the first person to read the book who had never met me and you had faith in the story and that it might help others to understand what it is to have a messy mind like me. Working with you has been a pleasure, thank you ever so much.

13. The Reader
Last, but not least, to you, my reader. If you manage to get to this point in the story, I congratulate you. It has not been easy.

Thank you for coming on this journey with me. Thank you for sticking with Jane, even when she did not want to stick with herself. Thank you for your patience, for your time and for your resilience; it is never easy reading a story without an ending, yet you have, nevertheless, continued to have faith in your narrator. Thank you for not giving up on me and thank you for not giving up on her, because, somewhere out there is a little girl, living in a semi-detached house in a sweet English village where a Magnolia tree weeps into a lawn each and every year. A little black-haired seven-year-old, who dreams of being a writer. That little girl has no idea what she will write about, no idea who she will conjure up in her imagination to occupy a world she has only ever dreamed of, but life will give her her story and, one day, she will have the courage to write it down. You have read the story, you have made her dreams a reality. So, thank you, dear reader, for not only being the reality of a Little Red Balloon's childish aspirations, but also, for choosing to read my story, a story I could not have written if I hadn't chosen life.